NONCONFORMIST COMMUNION PLATE

and

OTHER VESSELS

CAMDEN, Eagle Street (99) One of a set of twelve cups 1734. H 7¼ in.

NONCONFORMIST COMMUNION PLATE

and

OTHER VESSELS

Christopher Stell

OCCASIONAL PUBLICATIONS 4

THE CHAPELS SOCIETY

LONDON

2008

THE CHAPELS SOCIETY

website: www.britarch.ac.uk/chapelsoc/

HON. SECRETARY
Sara Crofts
47 Salisbury Drive
Midway
Swadlincote
Derbyshire
DE11 7LD

HON. EDITOR
Chris Skidmore
31 Melrose Avenue
Reading
RG6 7BN

ISBN: 978-0-9545061-2-4
ISSN: 1475-6404

PRODUCED IN GREAT BRITAIN FOR THE CHAPELS SOCIETY
BY OBLONG CREATIVE LTD, 416B THORP ARCH ESTATE, WETHERBY LS23 7BJ

CONTENTS

PREFACE

THIS MONOGRAPH originated as a by-product of the investigation into Nonconformist Chapels and Meeting-houses commenced by the author in 1967 and continued under the authority of the Royal Commission on the Historical Monuments of England with the encouragement of the then Secretary Mr A. R. Dufty. Four Inventory volumes embracing the whole of England were completed and published, not without much trial and tribulation, between 1986 and 2002. By the latter date the name and duties of the Royal Commission had been subsumed within the Historic Buildings and Monuments Commission for England, also known as 'English Heritage' and direct interest in communion plate, in particular, seemed no longer to be regarded as within their remit.

The *Inventory of Nonconformist Chapels and Meeting-houses* to which further reference will be made, while particularly concerned with the built inheritance of dissent also included brief references to various fittings of note including some of the more important items of church plate. The intention of publishing further material on these items and specifically an inventory of communion plate was intimated in the preface to the first volume (*Central England*, 1986), and the present publication is offered in fulfillment of that commitment. The Introduction which follows is based on the text of a paper read to the Society of Antiquaries of London in 1974 with considerable revision and enlargement to take account of the many further examples which were subsequently recorded.

The accompanying Inventory does not pretend to be an exhaustive list of all the plate in the possession of the various nonconformist churches of England. At best it may be claimed as representative of the many and varied items which have been found acceptable in differing circumstances over the past three centuries. Although no opportunity was lost in recording whatever plate might happened to be available, particular attention was given to seeking out and noting items known from published and other sources. The returns of some denominational questionnaires were inspected and particular efforts made to find items once recorded but whose location was no longer known. Published information particularly regarding the older Presbyterian or Unitarian congregations has been most prolific but other denominations of similar antiquity, though generally less well endowed, undoubtedly still retain more items of interest than this survey shows. The wisdom of drawing attention to congregational treasures may unfortunately have adverse results in tempting their owners or others to dispose of their patrimony. Thus it is timely to remind all churches of the need to ensure the safekeeping of their inheritance which is a tangible link to their forbears and an heirloom for their successors, not merely 'reserve capital' as one church treasurer unkindly described it.

In recording plate and related items no special consideration has been given to its intrinsic value and its historical significance has been paramount. For convenience and the avoidance of repetition silver may assumed unless otherwise stated and confirmed where possible by its assay marks; but pewter and base metal have not been ignored. Particular attention was given to recording any items, however insignificant, which carried inscriptions or other distinguishing marks of origin or of present or previous ownership. Assay and makers' marks have been recorded and compared with other published records, although the interpretation of worn or nearly illegible marks may leave a rich field for further opinions. Caution has therefore been observed in suggesting the names of silversmiths and pewterers where subtle differences can lead to erroneous conclusions. Most of the items listed were photographed and the illustrations included here are representative of a much larger archive which it is hoped will be transferred to a suitable repository.

Given the period over which this work has extended it is impossible to make full and adequate acknowledgement of all those persons who have in one way or another assisted with various aspects of this work. Many friends and colleagues whose advice or support has been freely given have already been named in previous publications. Especially appreciated are many whose wise counsels ensured the successful, if belated, completion of the four Inventory volumes.

In the matter of communion plate the author is particularly grateful to innumerable ministers, church treasurers, or other officials in whose care these vessels remain and whose interested and generous help was given, often after the shortest of notice, to permit their inspection and photography. It would perhaps be invidious to attempt to name many of those whom time may now sadly have moved on, though, for example, I recall with pleasure a centenarian treasurer in Dover as one of the more memorable patriarchs who so kindly gave up their time in the cause.

Several museum curators have generously permitted the closer inspection of their exhibits, notably in Birmingham, Exeter, Norwich, London, Southampton, and York. Two cups now amongst the Civic Plate of Colchester were also kindly made available. Particular thanks are as always due to the staff of Dr Williams's Library, where the trustees possess several interesting items from London congregations. The Unitarian authorities at Essex Hall generously produced several items which had been passed to them for safe-keeping from former congregations, though sadly some of these were later lost by theft.

The large accumulation of plate from orthodox Presbyterian churches formerly in the possession of the Presbyterian (now URC) Historical Society was seen and catalogued through the good offices of Mr R. J. Watson, together with the important collection of communion tokens some of which are illustrated here. Another large accumulation of plate was inspected at the former Congregational college at Whalley Range,

Manchester, where the principal the Revd R. J. McKelvey helpfully arranged access.

A few other individuals whose particular help is acknowledged include the late Canon Peter Hawker who enabled the inspection of the Kirkstead plate in Lincoln Cathedral Treasury. At an early stage in this exercise I was indebted to the Revd Andrew Hill, former secretary of the Unitarian Historical Society, for access to the returns of a census of plate from his denomination. At a similar distance of time I was assisted by Mr Pat Womersley, of Halifax, later of York, whose encouragement and interest were greatly appreciated. More recently I have had the benefit of the expertise of Ann Eatwell and her colleagues from the Department of Metalwork at the Victoria and Albert Museum, although it is feared that the urgent need to avoid further delay in publication has sadly prevented a greater reference to their extensive authority in this field. Many photographs taken by the Royal Commission photographers have been included here, for permission to use them and for providing copies of these and others the assistance of English Heritage is gratefully acknowledged.

Finally particular thanks are due to generosity of the Chapels Society in undertaking the publication of this record, to their Editor, Dr Chris Skidmore, and to Derek Brown at Oblong Creative Ltd, with all of whom it has ever been a pleasure to work.

C. F. S.

INTRODUCTION

CHURCH PLATE has been the subject of much scholarly attention over the past century or more; diocesan lists of plate in the possession of the Established Church of England have been compiled and published with great assiduity. Secular vessels belonging to a variety of public bodies as well as domestic collections have similarly been catalogued and discussed by many learned and respected authorities. Examples of all types are to be found in museums and art galleries, as well as in the more recently formed cathedral treasuries, although private collectors are understandably more reticent in advertising their possessions, making the locating of some items difficult if not impossible once they have passed through the sale rooms.

Conversely the communion plate belonging to the various nonconformist churches in England, which is the subject of the present memoir, has attracted comparatively little attention outside the individual denominations concerned and then more often for its supposed monetary value than for its greater historical importance as a tangible link with the benefactors and early supporters of a church or congregation. Apart from occasional references to plate in histories of individual congregations the widespread assumption seems to have been that such items could be of little general interest, as it was with the chapels themselves, long derided or ignored both within and outside organized dissent.

The first serious attempt to record a major portion of plate from any nonconformist denomination was undertaken in the late nineteenth century by the antiquary George Eyre Evans (1857–1939). His survey was restricted to 'Unitarian' churches which principally included many of Presbyterian origin and which attracted support from some of the more wealthy dissenters who were best able and inclined to provide themselves with plate suited to their needs and aspirations. Evans was the son of a Unitarian minister at Colyton, Devon, and was for a time minister at Whitchurch, Shropshire. He also later served as archaeology officer for the Royal Commission on Ancient Monuments in Wales and Monmouthshire from its commencement. His most important publication was *Vestiges of Protestant Dissent* (1897) which lists the ministers, church records

and, most importantly, the plate, much of which he was able to inspect in a great variety of locations; these he described as 'from banker's and jeweller's vaults in the bowels of the earth to the modest bandbox under the caretaker's bed ... and from the coal-hole under the grave-digger's tools, to the safe in a grocer's shop'. Evans repeated some of this information with additions in a series 'Our Communion Plate and other Treasures' in the *Transactions of the Unitarian Historical Society*, vols. IV–VII, which ceased at his death. A further valuable addition to the study of nonconformist plate was made by Edward Alfred Jones FSA in two articles in the first volume of *The Magazine of Fine Arts* (1905–6), 'Some Old Silver Communion Plate of English Nonconformity'. In these, which include a few references to other denominations, due acknowledgment is made to Evans' pioneering work in this field. A few other references appear in some of the earlier numbers of the *Transactions* of the Congregational Historical Society.

The Sacrament of the Lord's Supper, although held in high regard by most orthodox dissenters, was for long a cause of dissension and division. In the early years of the Puritan movement it was at the centre of disputes over the use of vestments and the mode of its administration and reception. The Quakers did not regard its observation as prescriptive, but the Presbyterians, Independents and Baptists, while differing over its frequency of observation, often restricted access to church members. Nightingale, the historian of Nonconformity in Lancashire, relates how Lord Willoughby, a chief supporter of Rivington Chapel, Lancashire, was once refused access to communion when on a chance visit to a village chapel, of unstated denomination, in the absence of acceptable credentials (Nightingale (1892) vol. 3, p. 91). This difficulty was overcome amongst the Calvinistic Presbyterians of Scotland and the extreme North of England by the issue of small metal tokens some examples of which from England are illustrated here (See *Communion tokens* below and Plates 32 and 33). These were generally distributed at a prayer meeting in a week prior to a communion service. In other congregations tickets were issued to be delivered up on attending the service as a means of regulating the attendance, and

Methodists made use of Class Tickets of membership for a similar purpose.

The general mode of administration of communion amongst the older Free Churches has been for the deacons or administrators to bring the elements to the individual participants at their seats. In Wesleyan Methodist tradition, in deference to their founder's views, which originally encouraged attendance at the parish churches, the communion continued to be observed at a communion rail.

BASIC NEEDS AND SMALL CUPS

The three main categories of vessel usually required for communion and listed here are cups, of many types and styles, flagons and plates. The record is not restricted to silver; pewter and other base metals are frequently found and were much favoured by less wealthy churches. This opportunity has also been taken to include reference to some other items of church metalwork, such as alms-dishes and a few baptismal basins. Many of the numerous pewter plates recorded may have been put to a variety of uses. Pottery cups such as Methodist and Moravian love-feast cups are generally excluded except where evidence of a possible communion purpose exists.

It is sometimes objected that much nonconformist 'plate' (to use this term in a general manner) is of domestic origin. How much that is so may now be more clearly seen. But this, too, tells a story of the origins of congregations, the growth of church fellowships and the generosity of benefactors, whose inscriptions and shields-of-arms adorn plate both old and new. Small country congregations and newly-founded causes often had of necessity to be satisfied with the barest of essentials and even the simplest of glass vessels have been found serving as communion cups. Thus the former Baptist church at Crockerton Green in Wiltshire (290)* was, when inspected in 1970, using a common glass 'rummer' to supplement or supersede a plain single-handled mug. The Congregational church in Farnham, Surrey (258), formed 1792, has a small eighteenth-century glass mug claimed to have been used in the early years of the church. Again, the Strict Baptists at Waddesdon Hill, Buckinghamshire, found their needs were served by a couple of small nineteenth-century wine glasses which were abandoned in the vestry cupboard when the church disbanded.

Some rural congregations of the late seventeenth or early eighteenth century were fortunate in finding on the shelves of their supporters cups which, though small and in some ways unsuitable, were nevertheless of a moderate artistic as well as intrinsic value. Where elsewhere a modest pewter cup might have been the height of expectation, at Platt Chapel, in the suburbs of Manchester (Plate 1A)† was located one of the earliest and smallest of two-handled cups, a little over two inches high, an early work of 1641 by Thomas Maundy. Two other small two-handled cups of 1658, comparable with the one at Platt but with slightly more elaborate handles and repoussé ornament in the base, were part of the plate belonging to the Independent church at Briston and Guestwick in Norfolk (Plate 1B, C) but now sadly dispersed. The date at which these small cups came into the possession of the respective congregations is indeterminate but from their size they could hardly have served satisfactorily other than small or rather exclusive communities. The probability that these vessels may initially have been in private hands will also be observed in numerous other instances such as the small two-handled cup of 1677 from Bradfield, Norfolk (Swafield (189), Plate 1D) given to the church in 1737.

BEAKERS

A more practicable form of vessel of which several examples are known is the beaker, an early example of which is a plain rather squat cup of 1658 from Kirkstead Abbey Chapel, Lincolnshire (177) a mediæval chapel occupied for a time by a Presbyterian congregation. The cup bears the initials of Henry and Jane Fines whose floor slab remains in the chapel. The most important series of silver beakers must have been that which belonged to the Independent church in Great Yarmouth, Norfolk (182) a church which originated in a joint congregation based in Norwich and Yarmouth but which soon resolved itself into two distinct parts. The Great Yarmouth church possessed, at least in the early eighteenth century, what must have been one of the most extensive sets of communion beakers in existence, comprising thirteen cups in all, besides other items. Many of these seem to have dated from 1654 (*pace* Evans) although two were slightly earlier. In the course of time, as so often happened amongst the older dissenting congregations, the church again divided, ostensibly over the choice of a minister but with the strong winds of disputed doctrine fanning the flames. This was no peaceful separation, but if the contending parties could not settle their differences they were at least able to divide the spoils, and a memorandum amongst the church papers more fully transcribed by

---

* Numbers in brackets refer to the relevant entry in the Inventory, commencing on page 9.
† Plates are found following page 8.

J. E. Clowes (1912, p. 69) brings the scene vividly to light:

The representatives of the orthodox sat on one side of the table, and Mr Ives on behalf of the other section opposite 'with whom' as the note says 'we argued the case, and came to agreement to divide the plate between us, which we concurred in; we told him there were thirteen silver beakers, two silver tankards, one silver flagon, we set six beakers and two tankards on one side, seven beakers and the flagon on the other and asked him which he would have, he replied "the six beakers and two tankards"; we told him he should have them. Accordingly he sent Mr Clarke and we delivered the six beakers and two tankards. There were seven pewter plates, he had four we kept three, there were two board-cloths and two napkins, he had one of each, and carried them away the 29th April, 1732, and do still remain in their custody'.

Mr Ives and his friends continued to occupy the Old Meeting-house which still remains, though rebuilt, on the original site and now 'Unitarian', while the orthodox party built a new meeting-house nearby and came to describe themselves as 'Congregational'. The sad tale of the Yarmouth beakers may briefly be concluded by noting that not a single one survives in the possession of either party. The share of the Old Meeting was inspected by G. E. Evans in 1894 but sold *circa* 1900; that of the New Meeting (Plate 2A) was sold in 1926 although some replicas were made.

Next in importance is a set of four beakers claimed to have been given 'about 1694' to a church meeting in Deadman's Place in Southwark (Plate 2B) by its pastor Jonathan Owen; of these the earliest dates from 1691, the others being late eighteenth-century replicas. Each has an engraved band of floral decoration around the rim. These are now in the Victoria and Albert Museum in London. Another set of four seventeenth-century beakers, unfortunately unlocated, belonged to the church at Hare Court in London (Plate 3A). Three of these were engraved with the shields-of-arms of the donors. Two small beakers belonging to a congregation in Ilminster, Somerset (Plate 3B, C) are more elaborately embossed, one of 1671 with floral ornament, the other of 1701 which has an Exeter assay mark has more formal gadrooning at the base. Comparable with these are the two beakers from a long lost congregation in South Petherton, Somerset (Plate 3D) the earlier cup again having embossed leaf ornament while the slightly later one of 1697 is more formally decorated with a band of acanthus leaves above the base.

The late eighteenth century is represented by a set of four plain beakers of 1763 from Halesworth, Suffolk (Plate 4A) although possibly originating from Walpole. Also from eastern England is a fine set of four elegantly tall and plain beakers at Lion Walk, Colchester (Plate 4B, C) with the assay letter for 1754/5 and proudly inscribed below the base with the date of acquisition, 1755. Probably of a similar date are a pair of plain beakers from Rendham, Suffolk (Plate 4D) in Sheffield plate. Also notable, and of particular transatlantic interest, is the beaker of 1772 from a church in Massachusetts (Plate 4E) given to a Congregational church in Uxbridge in 1930 and which may well have been one of a larger set.

Beakers do not figure greatly in Anglican plate or may have been dismissed as not being properly items of *church* as distinct from *secular* plate. It is therefore worth noting that they do occur in some quantity amongst plate in the Church of Scotland, although their distribution there is restricted to the north-east of the country where, as Thomas Burns observes (1892, p. 291) trade relations by sea with the Low Countries encouraged continental influence and introduced a form of cup also common in Holland. Although the number of beakers noted from English dissenting churches is small it is surely significant that most are found on the eastern side of the country where similar religious and trade links obtained.

STANDING CUPS

It is rather surprising that the beaker did not become more popular amongst English nonconformists. There can, however, be little doubt that the vessel most favoured was the two-handled communion cup which was similarly of domestic origin. But, firstly, and slightly earlier in dates of manufacture, the standing cup on a baluster stem without handles also appears in considerable numbers and forms some of the oldest items of chapel plate. Of these the earliest from Plymouth (Plate 5A) is dated 1632, being one of two cups bought in 1705. Others which are dated up to 1660 include a pair of cups of 1652–3 from Chowbent, Lancashire (Plate 7A) which may have been first used in the chapel-of-ease at Atherton which dissenters successfully retained in their possession until 1721. Undoubtedly in use from an early date were the two cups belonging to George's Meeting in Exeter (Plate 6A) of 1636 and 1660 and first used in its predecessor James's Meeting, with which name they are inscribed. The two cups are much alike, differing only in the shape of the bowl, the latter being more angular. A similar progression may be seen in the shape of the bowl in the magnificent series of four cups from the Great Meeting in Bideford, Devon (Plate 5B) of which the earliest is 1634 although all appear to have been in domestic use before being given to the church in the early or mid eighteenth century.

Other examples of this type of cup (Plate 7C) are to be found at Paul's Meeting, Taunton, Somerset of 1634, Bavington, Northumberland (Plate 6B) of 1655 and 1658, and at Chinley Chapel, Derbyshire (Plate 7B) of 1637. The pair of cups at Claypath, County Durham (Plate 7D), of 1647, is of interest in having more elaborate decoration of stylized leaves around the bowl and a later inscription dated 1775, the probable date of donation. A late and outstanding version of this form of cup is seen at Warrington, Lancashire (Plate 10B), where one of two exceptionally tall cups, assay 1735, and another of like date, with clear marks of re-use and donatory inscriptions added continue the traditional shape of the cup but in a still more elegant style.

Even later in date than the Warrington cups is the set of six very substantial cups from the old Independent Meeting-house in Norwich (Plate 8A) which were given to the church in 1757, the year of assay, and display a large and prominent inscription recording the name of the benefactor, Mr B. Balderston. Here the baluster-shaped stem is much bolder than in the earlier and more domestic versions of standing cups previously noted. This set was clearly intended to survive the rigours of use by a large number of worshippers and to be worthy of a society which now found itself in competition with the architectural presumption of the newly built Octagon Chapel nearby.

STANDING CUPS WITH HOLLOW STEM

A simpler and in some ways a more practical form of standing cup which found acceptance particularly in the first half of the eighteenth century had a relatively plain hollow stem often enriched with a small moulded band at mid height, though seldom of sufficient prominence to be seriously regarded as a 'knop'. The earliest notable set of cups of this type is, however, without any enrichment and the shape of the bowl is markedly angular above the stem. This is the set of six cups which belonged to the Independent church at the King's Weigh House in London (Plate 9A). Although alike in form these bear dates of manufacture from 1696 to 1705 and the earliest were probably acquired when in 1697 the church built a large meeting room above the King's Weigh House in Little Eastcheap. Another example of these undecorated cups, though more rounded in shape, is at Ross-on-Wye, Herefordshire, of 1706 (Plate 9B).

More frequent are those hollow-stemmed cups with an intermediate moulded band on the stem. Of these one of the most interesting sets is that from Bury St Edmunds, Suffolk (Plate 8B) where the Presbyterians erected a grand new meeting-house in 1711 and provided themselves with a full set of communion plate by Humphrey Payne, comprising four cups and four plates, all of which are now in the care of the civic authorities. The gift of this set by the minister to the trustees in 1720 may indicate that it was initially provided at his own cost. It also included at that date two large flagons which were probably of pewter and which were sold in 1747 for 3s 5d because, as the trust records relate, the then minister Dr Thomas Seward 'being in years could not well manage them'. A similar set of four cups of 1731 belonged to the Great Meeting in Coventry (276), but the most complete set comprising four cups, four plates and two flagons were given to the then Baptist church in Mary Street, Taunton, Somerset (Plate 10A) in 1744–5; in these the moulded band on the cups is more pronounced. This same style of cups also appears in the plate of formerly Presbyterian congregations at Colchester, Essex; Macclesfield, Cheshire; Cross Street, Manchester, Lancashire; and Chesterfield, Derbyshire. Similar, but with a deeper bowl in proportion to the total height are a pair of cups of 1725–6 at the Baptist Old Meeting-house in Blunham, Bedfordshire (Plate 10C), and others of 1715 are amongst the plate from the Congregational Meeting in Deptford, now in the Victoria and Albert Museum, London (Plate 9C). Most of these cups are undecorated or simply inscribed, but a pair of 1735 from Shrewsbury, Shropshire (Plate 10D) have a slightly more elaborate inscription within an oval frame.

Unique amongst the various forms of communion cup adopted by dissenting congregations is that which was presented to the Baptist congregation meeting in Eagle Street, London (Frontispiece, page ii) in 1734 by John Payne, one of the deacons. This set of twelve cups of 'hour-glass' form with a circular bowl and bell-shaped base separated by a spherical knop were sold to a purchaser in Canada following the dissolution of the church in 1961, one alone remaining with Bristol Baptist College. Another class of standing cups worthy of particular mention at this stage are the pewter cups in some of which, although often merely reproducing the familiar shapes already mentioned, a greater distinction is noticeable in the northern counties of England. There, in Cumberland, Durham and Northumberland, the influence of Scottish Presbyterianism was most extensively felt and some of the older congregations still looked northwards both for their preachers and their church polity. It is therefore not surprising that several of the earlier communion cups in particular which survived and which passed into the safe-keeping of the Presbyterian Historical Society of England (now part of the URC History Society) should exhibit a marked affinity with similar vessels then in use in the Church of Scotland. This resemblance is particularly evident (Plate 11A) in the thick moulded stems of a pair of standing cups from Haltwhistle, Northumberland dated 1745, a comparable pair from Harbottle in the same county dated 1766 (Plate 11C), and those from Whitehaven (Plate 11B).

PLAIN TWO-HANDLED CUPS

Probably the most recognizable type of communion cup found amongst English nonconformist congregations is the two-handled cup in various forms. The most frequent is the plain, undecorated cup with a pair of handles, on a moulded base with a vestigial stem and sometimes with an intermediate band of moulding encircling the bowl between the handles. Some of the earliest, such as one at Dukinfield, Cheshire (Plate 12A) of 1690 with its inscription recording its gift to the church by Samuel Angier in 1713, are small and the base very simply moulded. An example of a rather larger cup with a more pronounced base belongs to the Baptist church formerly meeting in Cote Chapel, Oxfordshire (Plate 12B) made in 1734 but given to the church forty years later. Better suited to a larger city congregation was a set of four plain and slightly taller cups from the Old Jury congregation in London (Plate 12C) made in 1728 with a slightly bolder moulding at the base and a matching inscription commemorating their purchase in that year. Another set of four cups, of 1727, belonged to the Presbyterian society at Lewins Mead in Bristol (85) and are modestly inscribed with the date of gift, 1728. At Little Carter Lane, London (Plate 12E), a new set of four cups was bought in 1766 which are very plain but inscribed beneath with the date of acquisition. A further set of four cups from a former London congregation in Monkwell Street (Plate 12D) illustrates the growing needs of a congregation which originally had a pair of cups of 1728–9, given in 1729, which carry a large inscription panel; to these a further two cups were added in 1735, similar to the first pair but with the inscription updated. The New Meeting in Birmingham (275) likewise bought a new set of four plain communion cups in 1782, now at Birmingham Art Gallery, which are tall but the capacity is reduced with a false internal lining.

An interesting though small number of cups of late eighteenth-century manufacture are notable for their sharply tapered bodies, almost V-shaped in fact, and have handles which rise high above the rim. Of these the plate belonging to the Octagon Chapel, Norwich (Plate 13A) is the most notable; these four cups of 1785 are also distinguished as the only cups which retain their original covers. An otherwise similar pair of cups belongs to St Mary's Chapel, Devizes, Wiltshire (Plate 13D) made in 1799 although bearing a pre-dated but later inscription. The pair of cups from Northgate End Chapel, Halifax, Yorkshire (Plate 13C) of 1792 are also in this style as is the notable set of eight cups belonging to the Great Meeting in Leicester (Plate 13B). The more sharply tapered bowl is also a feature of handle-less standing cups of this period.

Plain two-handled pewter or other base-metal cups also figure frequently amongst the possessions of the older nonconformist congregations. Examples of these include a pair of pewter cups of the early eighteenth century from Hale Chapel, Cheshire (25) and of rather later date a pair from a Baptist chapel at Sharnbrook in Bedfordshire (Plate 11D).

TWO-HANDLED GADROONED CUPS

More elaborate are the many two-handled cups with gadrooned decoration around the lower part of the bowl and often with a cable moulding below the rim and other embellishment usually in the form of a cartouche capable of taking an inscription or the initials of an owner or donor. One of the earliest examples of these in a simple form is a set of four cups of 1694 given in that year to the Scots Church which met at Founders' Hall in London (Plate 14A). Although devoid of a cartouche and modestly carrying the initials of their donors on their undersides they are evidence that their suitability for their intended purpose was accepted. Most of the thirty or so gadrooned cups noted date from between 1691 and 1729, the earliest being at Ipswich (Plate 14B), a very plain specimen lacking even the usual upper cable moulding. Later in that same very mixed collection is a cup of 1708 which sports a full cartouche carried below the cable moulding and a circular inscription panel with the donor's initials. A more spectacular set of four gadrooned cups is also to be found in Ipswich at Tacket Street (Plate 14C), the earliest of 1701 and a second of 1704, both have the cartouche over-riding the cable moulding as do the later two which are copies of the first, made in 1729 but all, including the replicas, carry the same inscription recording their donation in 1725. The gadrooned cup of 1703 given in 1746 to the congregation at Gateacre, Lancashire (Plate 14D) dispenses with the cable moulding but has a more prominently moulded base, as do two of the cups at Cambridge (Plate 15A). The more heavily moulded base also appears in a fine cup of 1705 given to Stand Chapel, Lancashire (Plate 15B) in 1759 by Margaret Walker whose initials with those of her husband William, who was master of Stand grammar school, appear in the oval frame of the cartouche and at the back is an inscription to record the gift. The cartouche is here unusually further embellished with the head of a rather hirsute cherub. A similar motif appears on a cup of 1714 by Nathaniel Lock at Haddenham Baptist chapel, Buckinghamshire (Plate 15C) given to the church in 1811. This type of gadrooned cup falls out of favour by the mid eighteenth century, but two late examples which belonged to the High Pavement Society in Nottingham (Plate 15D) date from 1752. A change to a rococo style of cartouche is also to be seen (Plate 16A) in a cup from the Independent Meeting in Ludlow, Shropshire made in 1768; this freedom of expression is also notable on a cup of 1764 at Rosslyn Hill Chapel, London, and on another at Upper Chapel, Sheffield, of 1784 (Plate 16B, C).

TWO-HANDLED CUPS, WITH REPOUSSÉ AND OTHER DECORATION

Another and less frequent version of the small two-handled cup has ogee-shaped sides and the lower part of the bowl is ornamented in repoussé with scenes of the chase. Three examples from High Street Chapel, Portsmouth (Plate 17) and now in the City Museum date from 1659 to 1669, one bearing a donatory inscription on the underside of 1718. A fine pair, very similar to the Portsmouth cups, dating from 1661 and 1668 belonging to the Old Meeting in Tenterden, Kent (Plate 18B, C, D) was regrettably sold in 1974 and a very similar pair of 1668 and 1676 was likewise disposed of by the trustees of Baffin's Lane Chapel, Chichester (266) about 1930. The only other cup decorated in this manner which was noted belonged to Platt Chapel, Manchester (Plate 18A); it bore the assay for 1660 and was simply ornamented with flowers and foliage but also had a cartouche on one face. This cup, also, was sold by the congregation in 1874 but repurchased and returned by two members of the church twenty-one years later. A similar fate met the only two-handled cup with acanthus ornament in repoussé from the Congregational Chapel in Newbury, Berkshire (7) reported to date from 1681, but sold with most of the plate of this old congregation in or about 1970.

Two further cups of rare occurrence are straight-sided two-handled cups engraved with oriental scenes (Plate 19). One of these belonged to the Independent Church at Guestwick, Norfolk and depicted a forest of tropical palms in which peacocks and other oriental birds disported themselves. This was sold with other items about 1980. The other is one of 1695, part of a mixed set belonging to the St Nicholas Street Meeting in Ipswich. It is also decorated with palms and a fountain.

MUGS OR SINGLE-HANDLED CUPS

Single-handled cups would hardly seem a very suitable choice for communion use, but a few examples appear some of which may have been converted from domestic use. The earliest of these are a pair from the former Presbyterian meeting at Tavistock Abbey Chapel, Devon (Plate 20A). These have straight sides with two moulded bands and strap handles. Similarly banded but with more substantial handles are a pair of 1704 by John Cory which belonged to the Old Meeting in Wareham, Dorset (Plate 20B). Of a similar date is the mug from Waterside Chapel, Newbury, Berkshire (Plate 20C), a fine specimen, now sadly lost, bearing a finely engraved achievement of arms and the donor's initials. A pair of mugs, closely resembling the pair from Tavistock, belongs to the Baptist church in Stow-on-the-Wold, Gloucestershire (Plate 20D). These date from 1709 and are particularly interesting being given, as the inscription indicates, specifically 'for the use of the Sacrament' although the date of gift is not stated. Of a slightly later period are the three mugs from the New Meeting in Kidderminster, Worcestershire (Plate 21A, B) where the earliest pair of 1721 and 1726 have relatively straight sides but that of 1793 has more rounded sides and greater elaboration in the handle. At Abingdon, Berkshire (Plate 21C, D), the mugs of 1761 and 1764, given to the church in the early nineteenth century, also exhibit these later characteristics.

TANKARDS

A very few small tankards have been noted. The late seventeenth-century flat-lidded tankards at Derby (43) and Oswestry (219) have been lost or sold, but a highly decorated flagon or tankard of 1770 given in 1849 to the Old Meeting in Ilminster, Somerset (Plate 22A) is notable; it probably served as a communion flagon. Less certain is the use of the two small tankards which together with a tall flagon and two plates constitute the new set of armorial plate given to the Old Meeting in Warminster, Wiltshire (Plate 22B–D) in 1790.

FLAGONS

The number of silver flagons recorded is relatively small in comparison with the frequency of silver cups and it may be supposed, as it has been with the flagons originally given to the Bury St Edmunds Presbyterians but later disposed of, that these were more often of pewter. Exceptionally, at Bristol in the late 18th century glass decanters were in use in place of flagons. Of surviving silver flagons the earliest is the first of two similar vessels in the possession of the Cross Street congregation in Manchester (Plate 23A). This dates from 1718 and is of traditional pattern with a tall body, widely splayed base and a domed lid but no distinct spout. It is very like a second one of 1752 and much resembles the pair of flagons of 1746 given, with other items, to the Mary Street Meeting in Taunton,

Somerset (Plate 23B) in that year. In great contrast with these is the very sophisticated though much more domestic shape of the flagon or jug of 1765 formerly belonging to the Baptist meeting in Eagle Street, London (Plate 23C) with its shaped body, prominent spout and covered handle. Much the same may be said of the ewer-shaped vessel of 1782 at Rosslyn Hill Chapel, London (Plate 23D) although that has an integral spout and is without a lid; in its general shape it matches the flagon from St Saviourgate Chapel in York (310) of 1790. More usual and acceptable was a continuation of the basic cylindrical body but with spout, wide base and domed lid as in the 1844 flagon from the King's Weigh House, London (Plate 24A) or that of 1845 from the Congregational chapel in Deptford, London (Plate 24B). A slightly more elaborate and later version of this tradition at St Mary's Chapel, Devizes (Plate 24C), of 1869, has a spout and, unusually, a moulded base and necking.

Several pewter flagons of interest (Plate 25), some of which are in the former Presbyterian Historical Society's collection, include one from Bewcastle in Cumberland, with a flat lid and inscribed date 1789 and the historically apposite touch of the pewterer Stephen Maxwell of a ship in full sail and the motto 'success to ye British Colonies'. Also, from Blyth in Northumberland, is a tall pewter flagon with a domed lid and a lengthy inscription dated 1777; this, together with a contemporary communion cup, closely match a similar pair, with the date 1769, at Falstone in the same county. Of later base metal and plated flagons little needs to be said except to note the frequent use which was made of them to carry often lengthy inscriptions as was done at Dover, Kent (Plate 24D) by the General Baptists to celebrate the passing of the Dissenters' Chapels Bill in 1844.

PLATES

Silver plates are not numerous although a few are worthy of particular notice; the earliest of 1663, at St Nicholas Street, Ipswich (250), and 1673 at St Saviourgate, York (Plate 26A), have distinctively broad rims and others of early date include one of 1688 at Mary Street, Taunton, which clearly passed through various owners before being given to the church in 1818. Several are raised on a central foot though some others have three small feet; variety is sometimes achieved by embellishing the rim with moulding or fashioning it in other ways. The opportunity is also often taken to engrave the details of a donation on the face of a plate as was done on the central boss or roundel of the two plates of 1705 and 1712 from James's Meeting, Exeter (Plate 26B) in 1746.

More frequently seen are the simple pewter plates which served many different functions even, as in a Friends' Meeting-house where no communion intention is to be inferred. Pewter plates are seldom dated except by reference to the touch of the pewterer where that is visible, although a few exceptions remain. For example, four plates at the Baptist chapel in Abingdon, Berkshire (Plate 26C) are inscribed on the rim with the date 1749 within a wreath; similarly, at the Baptist chapel at Hook Norton, Oxfordshire (Plate 26D) are two plates inscribed on the rim with the name of the church and the numerals '17..' of a possibly uncompleted date. Of more general interest, though clearly secular in origin, is the plate at Cam, Gloucestershire (Plate 26E) dated 1673. Broader or deeper dishes also exist which have been regarded as either alms-dishes or possibly as baptismal basins; of the former is one notable but sadly decayed example at Alnwick, Northumberland (193) dated 1689, with the apposite reminder to 'Remember the Poor'.

BAPTISMAL BASINS

While fonts and fontlets come only peripherally within the context of church plate a few silver or base metal basins deserve a mention. One of these is the fine silver basin from the King's Weigh House in London (Plate 27A) which dates from 1697. Another, from a former Presbyterian congregation in Trowbridge, Wiltshire (Plate 27B) is of 1767. A plain bowl of base metal from the former Countess of Huntingdon's Chapel at Fordham, Essex (Plate 27C) is presumed to have served a similar purpose. An oval bowl with two handles, in electroplate of the late nineteenth century, in the Moravian Chapel at Lower Wyke, Yorkshire (Plate 27D) is also of passing interest.

THE NINETEENTH CENTURY

Most of the items which have been discussed above date from the years prior to the opening of the nineteenth century. There are, however, a number of individual pieces as well as longer sets of plate from this latter period which deserve a mention even though the information needed to discuss them in greater depth is inadequate. While silverware continued to be desired and acquired where circumstances permitted the development of Sheffield plate and the introduction of such variants as 'Britannia Metal' met the increasing demands of growing and multiplying churches by the mid-nineteenth century. The development at that period of electroplating also reduced the cost and increased the availability of communion vessels while taking away some of the artistic character and individuality of earlier days.

A group of standing cups of the first decade of the nineteenth century, of minor interest, all having a square sub-base, though by different makers, include one of 1802 from Bolton, Lancashire (Plate 28A), four from Broad Street, Reading, Berkshire (Plate 28C) of 1805/10, and one from a Presbyterian congregation in Manchester (Plate 28B) of *circa* 1803. This last was the only piece of silver surviving amongst over two hundred items of plate in the collection of the former Presbyterian Historical Society when inspected by the author in 1970. Of similar size though of lesser capacity are the four tulip-shaped cups from Conigre Chapel, Trowbridge, Wiltshire (Plate 28D) which date from 1822. From the same county is the surprisingly elaborate thistle-shaped cup of 1833 (Plate 29A) and given to the Strict Baptists in Marlborough in 1848 shortly after the erection of Zion Chapel, whence it was transferred to Bradenstoke in 1921. An exceptional Gothic communion cup of 1840 found a home in Bowden Hill Chapel, Crediton, Devon (Plate 29B) as a donation in 1861. Anything less suitable for placing in an old meeting-house of such historic importance is hard to imagine but the Gothic imagery of gabled and crocketted arcading around the bowl, although unparalleled, is consistent with its date.

The needs of large and 'respectable' congregations are ably represented by several sets of communion plate from the North of England. The Methodist Society at Brunswick Chapel, Leeds (Plate 29C) had an impressive pair of cups, suitably engraved, together with a matching flagon and plates, all of Sheffield manufacture and dating from 1825–6. The Parish Church of St Andrew at Ramsbottom, Lancashire is exceptional in having been built for Presbyterian use and endowed with a set of plate for which the receipt survives. This set (Plate 30) remained with the church following the transfer of the building to the Church of England in 1871. On a more mundane level is a set of six cups (later extended to eight) together with plates and a pair of flagons, presented in 1840 for use in the newly rebuilt Great George Street Chapel, Liverpool (Plate 29D), then under the care of the celebrated Dr Raffles. These are all of Sheffield plate and of what might be described as a standard pattern. Quite a different matter was the set of plate given by the two secretaries of the Building Committee of the Congregational Church in Broughton Park, Salford (Plate 31) for use in their new building, once one of the most distinctive nonconformist monuments in North-west England. This set of four cups, four plates and a flagon, all of 1874 by Elkington & Co. of Manchester, represents a serious attempt to

follow mediæval precedent with chalice-like cups, a narrow necked flagon and highly decorated plates. But whether this tells us anything of a change in communion practice or belief other than a desire to be in the forefront of fashion may be debatable. At any rate the general nonconformist acceptance of the 'common cup' began to be seriously eroded by the gradual introduction of individual communion glasses, mainly on the initiative of the Revd John Henry Jowett of Birmingham from about 1905. Significantly thirteen trays of these tiny cups, by Townshends Ltd of Birmingham, dated 1905, were added to the Broughton Park possessions, rendering the earlier cups redundant or merely symbolic.

The coming of individual communion glasses and their rapid spread through most nonconformist denominations has been one of the factors threatening the survival of much early or interesting nonconformist plate. The sale of church silver has been such a temptation to church treasurers to balance their books and to unrestrained members to exhibit their disavowal of worldly goods that, combined with carelessness, failure to take reasonable precautions and simple theft, much has been lost over the past century. The list that follows cannot be complete but it emphasizes the present or recent state of the still rapidly diminishing stock of nonconformist family silver.

COMMUNION TOKENS (Plates 32 and 33)

Some items closely associated with the practice of Communion, although most frequently in use by the Calvinistic Presbyterians of Scotland, which are worthy of inclusion as a postscript are the metal discs by which pastors regulated and controlled attendance at the infrequent celebration of the Sacrament. Presbyterian congregations in the northern counties of England looked to North Britain for their pulpit supplies and their form of church government and naturally adopted similar customs. The selection of tokens illustrated is from the collection of the former Presbyterian Historical Society of England. Many particularly of the earlier ones are cast in lead and carry the initials of ministers. The earliest, from Falstone, is an exception in being heart-shaped; most are round or square with oval specimens coming on later. The dish-shaped token from Barrington is also exceptional. Some have representations of the chapels, two of which in this group are from Manchester, the third illustrates the front of Swallow Street chapel of 1801–4 which stood in a narrow alley off Piccadilly, in London.

PLATE I   Small two-handled cups, 17th-century

A. MANCHESTER, Platt Chapel (156)
1641 by Thomas Maundy. H 2¼ in.

B. BRISTON (180) 1658. H 2⅛ in.

C. Interior of (B). Overall W 5¼ in.

D. SWAFIELD (189) 1677. H 2⅝ in.

PLATE 2   Beakers

A. GREAT YARMOUTH, New Meeting (183) early 17th-century (H 6⅜ in.) and 1654 (H 5½ in.)

B. SOUTHWARK (115) Set of four, *circa* 1691 and late 18th-century. H 5¼ in.

PLATE 3   Beakers

HARECOURT COMMUNION PLATE.

1. Sir Bulstrode Whitelocke's Plate.   2. Plate, the gift of a Widow Lady.   3. Sir Robert Tichborne's Cup.
4. Cup, with the Arms (probably) of a Miss Champneys.   5. Cup, with the Arms (probably) of Thomas Fletcher, Esq.

A. ISLINGTON, Hare Court
(111) 17th-century plate, from
Marsh (1871)

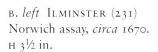

B. *left* ILMINSTER (231)
Norwich assay, *circa* 1670.
H 3½ in.

C. *right* ILMINSTER (231) 1701
by J. Elston. H 3½ in.

D. SOUTH PETHERTON (234)
left 1697 by William Andrews
H 3⅜ in.
right 1691. H 3⅜ in.

PLATE 4 Beakers, 18th-century

A. *right* HALESWORTH (248) 1763 by Thomas Whipman & Charles Wright. H 4⅜ in.

B. *below* COLCHESTER (79) 1754 by Walter Brind. H 5½ in.

C. *bottom left* Inscribed base of (B)

D. *bottom centre* RENDHAM (252) Mid-18th-century. H 5½ in.

E. *bottom right* HILLINGDON (109) Beaker from Uxbridge, Mass. *circa* 1772. H 5¾ in.

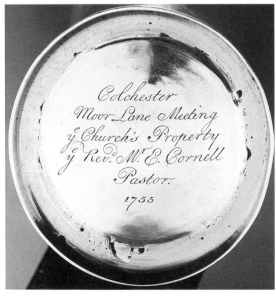

PLATE 5   Standing cups, 17th-century

A. PLYMOUTH (59)
left 1632 (H 6¾ in.),
right 1660 or 1662
(H 7 in.)

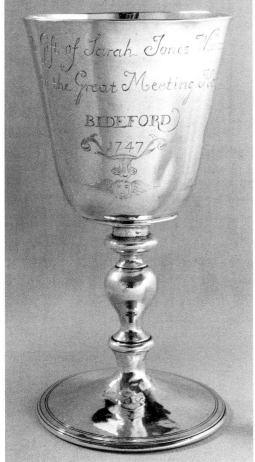 

B. BIDEFORD (47)
left 1634 (H 7½ in.),
right circa 1675
(H 6⅜ in.)

PLATE 6 Standing cups, 17th-century

A. EXETER (51)
From James's
Meeting
left 1636. H 7⅛ in.
right 1660. H 6¾ in.

B. BAVINGTON
(194) Two cups
from Great
Bavington
left 1655. H 6⅝ in.
right 1658. H 6½ in.

PLATE 7   Standing cups, 17th-century

A. *left* ATHERTON,
Chowbent (140) 'Mort
Cup', 1652. H 6¾ in.

B. *right* CHINLEY (42)
1637. H 6⅞ in.

C. *left* TAUNTON (236)
1634. H 7¾ in.

D. *right* DURHAM (73)
1647. H 5⅜ in.

PLATE 8   Standing cups with hollow stems, 18th-century

A. NORWICH, Old Meeting (187) Set of six, 1757 by ?John Wirgman. H 10 in.

B. BURY ST EDMUNDS (244) 1711 by Humphrey Payne. Cups H 7½–7¾ in.

PLATE 9 Standing cups with hollow stems, 17th- and 18th-century

A. *left* WESTMINSTER (118) 1696 by John Sutton. H 8¾ in.

B. *right* ROSS ON WYE (124) 1706 by Humphrey Payne. H 7⅛ in.

C. LEWISHAM, Deptford (114) 1715 by Matthew Lofthouse. H 9½ in.

PLATE 10   Standing cups with hollow stems, 18th-century

A. TAUNTON (235) 1746 by Humphrey Payne. H 9 in.

B. WARRINGTON (169) 1735.
H 10 in.

C. BLUNHAM (1) 1725. H 7⅜ in.

D. SHREWSBURY (220) 1735 by
Humphrey Payne. H 8⅝ in.

PLATE 11   Pewter cups, 18th-century

A. *top left* HALTWHISTLE (202) Dated 1745. H 7⅝ in.

B. *top right* WHITEHAVEN (38) Mid-18th-century. H 8¼ in.

C. *left* HARBOTTLE (203) Dated 1766. H 8½ in.

D. *above* SHARNBROOK (2) *circa* 1800 by Carpenter & Hamberger. H 5½ in.

PLATE 12   Plain two-handled cups

A. DUKINFIELD (23) 1690. H 4¼ in.

B. COTE (213) 1734 by Francis Spilsbury. H 5½ in.

C. LONDON, Old Jury (95) 1728 by Gabriel Sleath. H 5⅛ in.

D. LONDON, Monkwell Street (94) 1728. H 6½ in.

E. ISLINGTON (110) 1766 by Thomas Whipham & Charles Wright. H 5¾ in.

PLATE 13   Later 18th-century two-handled cups

A. *left* NORWICH (188) 1785. H rim 7¼, to finial 10¾ in.

B. *above* LEICESTER (171) 1786 by Robert Hennell. H rim 6½, handles 7 in.

C. HALIFAX (323) 1792 by Henry Chawner. H rim 6½, handles 7⅛ in.

D. DEVIZES (287) 1799 by ?John Harris. H 9½ in. overall

PLATE 14   Gadrooned two-handled cups

A. LONDON, Founders' Hall (93)
1694. H 4¼ in.

B. *right* IPSWICH, St Nicholas
Street (250) 1691. H 4¼ in.

C. *below left* IPSWICH, Tacket
Street (251) 1701 by
John Smithsend. H 3⅞ in.

D. *below right* LIVERPOOL,
Gateacre (152) 1703 by
Alice Sheene. H 5 in.

PLATE 15 Gadrooned two-handled cups

A. *above left* CAMBRIDGE (16) 1705 by John Cory. H 4½ in.

B. *above right* RADCLIFFE, Stand Chapel (163) 1705 by ?John Wisdome. H 4¾ in.

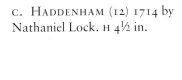

C. HADDENHAM (12) 1714 by Nathaniel Lock. H 4½ in.

D. NOTTINGHAM (210) 1752 by Fuller White. H 4¼ in.

PLATE 16   Gadrooned two-handled cups

A. LUDLOW (217) 1768.
H 4⅝ in.

B. CAMDEN, Rosslyn Hill
(101) cup (ii) 1764 by
William Cripps. H 3½ in.

C. SHEFFIELD, Upper
Chapel (336) cup (ii) 1784
by ?James Young. H 5 in.

PLATE 17   Two-handled cups with repoussé decoration

PORTSMOUTH, High Street Chapel (121)

A. *left* Cup (i) 1659, unicorn. H 3¾ in.

B. *below left* Same cup, opposite face with hunting dog

C. *above right* Cup (ii) 1668, stag. H 3 in.

D. *left* Same cup, opposite face with dog

PLATE 18   Two-handled cups with repoussé decoration

A.   MANCHESTER, Platt Chapel
(156) 1660. H 3¾ in.

B. *right* TENTERDEN (138)
Cup (i) 1661. H 3⅜ in.

C. *below left* TENTERDEN (138)
Cup (ii) 1668. H 3½ in.

D. *below right* Same cup,
opposite face with hunting dog

PLATE 19   Two-handled cups with oriental decoration

A. GUESTWICK
(184) Cup (i) 1683.
H 3⅛ in.

B. *left* IPSWICH,
St Nicholas Street
(250) Cup (ii) 1695.
H 4 in.

C. *below left*
GUESTWICK (184)
same cup as A,
opposite face with
palm tree

D. *below right*
IPSWICH,
St Nicholas Street
(250) same cup as B,
opposite face with
fountain

PLATE 20 Mugs

A. TAVISTOCK (61) late 17th-century. H 3⅜ in.

B. WAREHAM (72) 1704 by John Cory. H 4⅝ in.

C. NEWBURY (6) 'The Bunney Mug', 1705 by John Rand. H 4⅛ in.

D. STOW-ON-THE-WOLD (89) 1709 by ?George Cox. H 3⅛ in.

PLATE 21   Mugs

A. KIDDERMINSTER (306) Cup (i) 1721 by
Thomas Farren. H 4 in.

B. KIDDERMINSTER (306) Cup (iii) 1793 by
Charles Aldridge. H 4¾ in.

C. ABINGDON (4) Cup (i) 1761 by Thomas Whipham &
Charles Wright. H 5 in.

D. ABINGDON (4) Cup (ii) 1764 by W. & J. Deane.
H 5¼ in.

PLATE 22   Late 18th-century tankards, flagon, and plate

A. *top left* ILMINSTER (231) Tankard, 1770 by Thomas Parr. H 8½ in.

WARMINSTER (299)

B. *top right* Tankard, 1789 by ?Thomas Wright. H 8⅛ in.

C. *below left* Flagon, 1789, same maker. H 12⅝ in.

D. *below right* Plate, 1789 by ?James Young. D 9½ in.

PLATE 23   Flagons, 18th-century

A. *left* MANCHESTER (154) 1718 by Humphrey Payne. H 12 in.

B. *right* TAUNTON (235) 1746 by Humphrey Payne. H 11¾ in.

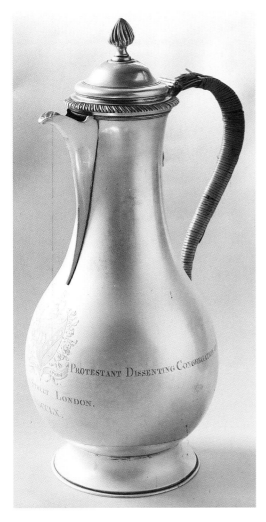

C. *left* CAMDEN, Eagle Street (99) 1765 by Francis Crump. H 15¼ in.

D. *right* CAMDEN, Rosslyn Hill (101) 1782 by John Scofield. H 12¼ in.

PLATE 24   Flagons, 19th century

A. *left* WESTMINSTER (118) 1844 by E., E. J. and W. Barnard. H 14 in.

B. *right* LEWISHAM, Deptford (114) 1845 by R. Pearce & G. Burrows. H 11¼ in.

C. *left* DEVIZES (287) 1869. H 12½ in.

D. *right* DOVER (135) Electroplate 1844 by Elkington and Co. H 11½ in.

PLATE 25   Pewter Flagons

A. BEWCASTLE (34) late 18th-century. H 10¼ in.

B. BAVINGTON (194) pre-1765 by
George Lowes. H 10¼ in.

C. BLYTH (198) *circa* 1777. H 13¼ in.

D. FALSTONE (200) *circa* 1769. H 13½ in.

PLATE 26   Plates and inscriptions

A. *top left* YORK, St Saviourgate (310) 1673, with donatory inscription, 1696

B. *top right* EXETER (51) Inscribed boss, plate from James's Meeting

C. *middle left* ABINGDON (3) 1749 inscription on pewter plate

D. *middle right* HOOK NORTON (214) 18th-century inscription on pewter plate

E. *bottom left* CAM (86) plate with amatory inscription, 1673

F. *bottom right* LYNEHAM (291) plate from Marlborough, donated 1848

PLATE 27 Baptismal Basins

A. WESTMINSTER (118) 1697
by Joseph Ward. D 9⅛ in.

B. *left* TROWBRIDGE (297)
1767 by Edward Aldridge.
D 8⅝ in.

C. *below left* FORDHAM (81)
late 18th-century, base metal.
W 10½ in.

D. *below right* WYKE (344)
late 19th-century, length
overall 15¼ in.

PLATE 28   Early 19th-century Communion Cups

A. *left* BOLTON (143)
1802 by Thomas
Lamborn. H 6¼ in.

B. *right* MANCHESTER
(157) Early
19th-century by John
Robertson. H 6¼ in.

C. *left* READING (8)
1805/10 by Charles
Chesterman. H 6¾ in.

D. *right* TROWBRIDGE
(296) Tulip cup, 1822
by ?Robert Peppin.
H 6⅜ in.

PLATE 29   19th-century Communion Cups

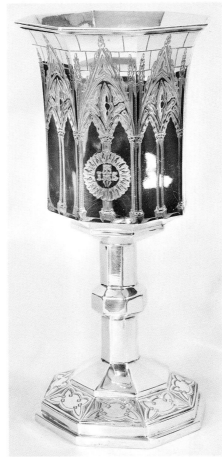

A. *left* LYNEHAM (291) Thistle cup, *circa* 1833. H 6¾ in.

B. *right* CREDITON (48) Gothic cup, 1840 by Joseph & John Angel. H 8 in.

C. *left* LEEDS (329) 1825 by S. Roberts, Smith and Co. H 7¾ in.

D. *right* LIVERPOOL (149) 1840, Sheffield plate. H 9⅛–9¼ in.

PLATE 30   Early 19th-century Communion Set

RAMSBOTTOM (165) 1833 by William Ker Reid for the
formerly Presbyterian St Andrew's Church

A. *above* Pair of cups. H 8⅜ in.

B. *right* Flagon. H 12 in.

C. *left* Alms dish. D 16 in.

D. *above* Baptismal basin. D 7¼ in.

PLATE 31   Late 19th-century Communion Set

SALFORD (167) 1874 by Elkington and Co. for Broughton Park Congregational Church

A. Cup. H 8 in.

B. Plate. D 9 in.

C. Flagon. H 12 in.

PLATE 32   English Presbyterian Communion Tokens

A selection of examples from the collection of the United Reformed Church History Society, reproduced full size. (*Above* obverse, reverse in Plate 33)

KEY TO PLATES 32 AND 33
(Numbers at the end of each entry refer to the item numbers in Herdman (1901))

TOP ROW
1. Falstone, Northumb., I. D. F for James Deane, Falstone, first minister, 1729. Lead. 72
2. Ford, Northumb., Crookham. C for Crookham, 1752. Lead. 57
3. Adderstone with Lucker, Northumb., Warrenford. D over WW for Warrenford, William Wright, second minister, 1755. Lead. 219
4. Ingram, Northumb., Branton. B for Branton, 1756. Lead. 45
5. Sunderland, Durham, Monkwearmouth, North Bridge Street. MWMH for Monkwearmouth Meeting-house, 1779, IH for James Hope. Lead. 205
6. Tynemouth, Northumb., North Shields, Howard Street. H.M.N.S. for Hamilton Murray, North Shields, 'AD 1781'. Lead. 178
7. Newcastle upon Tyne, Northumb., Wall Knoll. WKNC for Wall Knoll, Newcastle, 'AD 1782'. Lead. 167

SECOND ROW
8. Whitby, Yorks. NR., Cliff Lane A.C. (Associate Congregation) Whitby, 1799. Rev. P. Thomson. Lead. 225
9. Rochester, Northumb., Birdhopecraig. TH over BC for Thomas Hope, Birdhopecraig, 1810. Lead. 35
10. Gateshead, Durham, Scotch Church. GC for Gateshead Chapel, 1818. Lead. 78
11. Glanton, Northumb. GM for Glanton Meeting, 1824. Lead. 80
12. Maryport, Cumb., John Street. WR for William Rentoul, fourth minister, 1825. Lead. 156
13. Alnwick, Northumb., Clayport Street, 1831. Brass. 1
14. Ingram, Northumb., Branton, 1845. White metal. 46

THIRD ROW
15. Longframlington, Northumb. Sa for Sacrament. Lead. 136
16. Bewcastle, Cumb. WL for William Lauder, minister 1788–99, 1809–32. Lead. 33
17. Bellingham, Northumb. ABB for Alexander Brown, Bellingham, first minister 1808–27. White metal. 18
18. Westminster, Gtr London, Scots Church, Swallow Street. White metal. [*Not in Herdman*]
19. Manchester, Lancs., Church of Scotland, 1832. White metal. 152
20. Manchester, Lancs., Lloyd Street Chapel, 1801. White metal [*Not in Herdman*]

BOTTOM ROW
21. Lowick, Northumb., Scotch Church. L for Lowick, IC for Israel Craig, minister 1793–1843. 150
22. Bavington, Northumb., Great Bavington. White metal. 10
23. Berwick-upon-Tweed, Northumb., Low Meeting. IC for John Crambe, minister 1824–36. Copper. 23
24. Stamfordham, Northumb. 'Communion'. White metal. 195
25. Manchester, Lancs., Grosvenor Square. White metal. 153

PLATE 33   English Presbyterian Communion Tokens

A selection of examples from the collection of the United Reformed Church History Society (reverse of samples in Plate 32)

ACKNOWLEDGEMENTS

Plates 2A, B; 3D; 4B, C; 6B; 7C; 8A, B; 9A, C; 10A; 11A, B, C; 12C, D, E; 13A, D; 14A; 16B; 18B, C, D; 20B, C; 22B, C, D; 23A, B, C, D; 24A, B, C; 25A, B, D; 26B, F; 27A, B; 28B, C, D; 29B; and all photographs in Plates 30, 31, 32 and 33 are Crown Copyright, English Heritage. All others are the author's copyright.

AN INVENTORY OF ENGLISH NONCONFORMIST PLATE

This Inventory is arranged in the order of English counties and civil parishes existing immediately prior to local government re-organization in 1974, consistently with the four volumes of the Inventory of Nonconformist Chapels and Meeting-houses *published by the Royal Commission on Historical Monuments (1986–2002). Numbers in square brackets following individual entries refer, where applicable, to the relevant monument numbers in the respective county section of the RCHM Inventory.*

References to item numbers in Cotterell (1929) Old Pewter its Makers and Marks *are indicated 'C.3732' &c; Jackson (1989) refers to the 3rd edition of* English Goldsmiths and Their Marks, *reprinted 2005, unless otherwise stated. Dimensions are given where possible in inches as measured to the nearest eighth and unless otherwise stated are:* H = height to rim; D = diameter at rim; W = width overall, particularly including handles. Dates of assay refer to the assay year commencing in May.*

BEDFORDSHIRE

(1) BLUNHAM, Old Meeting (Baptist). *Cups:* (Plate 10C) pair, long tapered bowl, everted rim, short hollow stem with moulded band and base. Inscribed 'B⁂C | 1726'. London 1725, Maker 'WP, pellet below', for William Paradise. H 7⅜, D 3¾; capacity one pint. [15]

(2) SHARNBROOK (Strict Baptist). *Cups:* (Plate 11D) pair, pewter, tapered bowl with moulded rim, centre band and base, two double-curved handles. 'Hall-marks' of Carpenter & Hamberger of London (C.182), *c.*1800. H 5½, D 4¼, W 8. *Plates:* pewter. (i) Inscribed 'W over I E' on rim. 'Hall-marks' of William Wette or Wetter of London (C.5073), late 17th-century. D 8⅞. (ii) Touch of Robert & Thomas Porteous 'successors to Richard King' (C.3732), late 18th-century. D 8⅞. (iii) Inscribed 'EW' on rim. 'Hall-marks' 'H; three stars and three mullets; lion passant; buckle', name not traced. D 9¼. [74]

BERKSHIRE

(3) ABINGDON, Ock Street (Baptist). *Cups:* four (i–ii) pair, straight sided bowl moulded rim and base, two handles. Inscribed underneath 'Ex Dono Benjamin Tomkins 1719'. London 1719, maker Gabriel Sleath. H 4¾, D 4, W 8; (iii) bowl rounded below with two bands, moulded base of double curved handles. London 1842, maker RW. H 5¼, D 4⅜, W 7¼. (iv) same

size and description as last but possibly Sheffield plate. Mark on base 'GS surmounted by fleur-de-lys and mural crown', mid-19th-century. *Flagon:* electroplate, inscribed 'Baptist Church Abingdon | R.H.Marten Pastor | J.Williams J.Burry | C.Coxeter | Deacons | 1851'. *Plates:* (Plate 26C) four, pewter. Inscribed on rim within a wreath 'Baptist Church | Abingdon | Berks | 1749'. Touch of John Langford of London on three, his 'hall-marks' on all four including initials FW (C.2823–4), mid-18th-century. D 9¾ (two); 10⅞ (two). [1]

(4) ABINGDON (Congregational/URC). *Cups:* three mugs with baluster-shaped bowl and double-curved handle, all given in early 19th century, slight variations in design. (i) (Plate 21C) Inscribed with initials '*JEG*' in monogram, and later inscription above and below '*The Gift of Miss Mary Peck | to the Church*', given to the church 1807. London 1761, makers Thomas Whipham & Charles Wright. H 5, D 3⅞, W 5. (ii) (Plate 21D) Later inscription '*The Gift of Mrs Wayght | to the Church*' and marked on base 'M over I S'. London 1764, makers William & John Deane. H 5¼, D 3¼, W 5⅞. [(iii) not inspected, reported to be inscribed '*The Gift of Mr Joseph Fletcher . . .*' and marked (? on base) 'B over R B'. London 1768, maker 'S.W, pellet between']. *Flagon:* base metal. Inscribed 'Independent |

Church | Abingdon | 1845'. [The three cups were reported stolen May 1974]　　　　　　　　　[3]

(5) MAIDENHEAD (Congregational/URC). *Cups*: four, bowl with S-shaped sides, short stem and moulded base, two handles. H 5¼, D 4, W 7. (i) London 1771, maker JS; (ii) London 1804, maker HS; (iii–iv) London 1838, maker C L. *Cups*: pair, pewter, tapered bowl with band, moulded stem and base. Inscribed on underside '*Meeting House Maidenhead 1784*'. H 7⅜, D 4⅛. [One now in Richardson collection, Truro Museum, Cornwall; the other formerly in Port collection (Cotterell (1929) pl. XXXc) now at V&A]. *Plates*: four (i–ii) pair, pewter. Touch of John Fasson of London (C.1636), mid-18th-century. (iii–iv) pair, pewter. Touch of Henry Sewdley of London (C.4193) but 'hall marks' of John Fryers (C.1791), early 18th-century.　　[37]

(6) NEWBURY, Waterside Chapel (Presbyterian/Unitarian). *Cups*: two mugs with moulded rim, upper band and base, hollow handle. H 4⅛, D 3⅛. (i) (Plate 20C) Engraved with shield-of-arms of Howard with crest and mantling, initials '*BB*' added above for Brice Bunney, donor. London 1705, maker 'Ra' for John Rand (Jackson (1989) 156); (ii) Facsimile of last but not engraved or inscribed. London 1848, maker 'J.E.' *Plates*: five (i) raised on central hollow stem with moulded band and base. London 1848, maker 'J.E' as above. H 3⅝, D 6¼. (ii–iii) London 1848, maker 'J.E' as above. D 9⅜. (iv–v) London 1792 and 1802, maker 'WB' for ?Walter Brind. D 5½. [Cup (i) and Plate (i) reported stolen from Essex Hall, London, August 1971]　　　　　　　　　　　　　[41]

(7) NEWBURY, Cromwell Place (Congregational/URC). *Cups*: four [(i) bowl with slight upstand at base and two barbed handles, repoussé decoration of acanthus leaves around lower half and band of plant stem ornament below rim. Inscription added below band '*The Gift of Mrs. Eliz. Merriman late of St.Thomas's Southwark who died March 20th 1780 to the Independent Meeting at Newbury*'. Reported as (?London) 1681, maker 'CK with mullet below'. (ii) bowl with plain S-shaped sides, slight upstand at base, and two barbed handles. Pricked inscription 'EM between scrolls', possibly original, and later inscription as above. London 1671, maker 'RS between mullets' (Jackson (1989) 132). H 3½.]. (iii) bowl with everted rim, shaped base and two strap handles. Inscribed 'INDEPENDENT CHURCH | NEWBURY'. London 1777, maker Walter Brind. H 4⅞, D 3⅝, W 6½. [(iv) similar to last. Apart from (iii) these and other items were sold locally in 1970 and have not been located; they are described from surviving photographs and a valuation note]　　　　　　　　　[42]

(8) READING, Broad Street (Congregational/URC). *Cups*: (Plate 28C) four, plain bowl on stem with reeded band, circular reeded base on square sub-base. London 1805 (two) and 1810 (two), maker Charles Chesterman. H 6¾, D 4⅛, base 3⅞ square.　　　[47]

BUCKINGHAMSHIRE

(9) BEACONSFIELD (Congregational/URC). *Plates*: four, pewter. (i–ii) Inscribed 'F over I M' on rim, touch and 'hall-marks' of John Tidmarsh of London (C.4742), 18th-century. D 9¼. (iii) Inscribed 'TG' on rim, touch and 'hall-marks' of John Watts of Tokenhouse Yard, London (C.4991), 18th-century. D 9¼. (iv) Rectangular touch below rim with name NICHOLSON (C.3397–3402), probably 18th-century. D 9⅝. [Summers (1900) 17–18, also records communion *cups* which 'originally belonged to the Old Meeting and bear the inscription "Baconsfield Meeting, 1781",' and a *flagon* which 'belonged to Bethesda Chapel', i.e. early 19th-century. These items are no longer in the possession of the church].　　　[10]

(10) CHESHAM (Congregational/URC). *Cups*: pair, everted rim, stem with moulded band, moulded base. Engraved with shield-of-arms in a wreath and inscribed '*The Gift of Mrs Ann Skottowe to the Independent church at Chesham under the Pastoral Care of The Revd: Mr. Spooner 1774*'. London 1774, maker 'CW', possibly Charles Wright. H 8⅞, D 4⅜. *Flagon*: cup-shaped body with narrow neck, spout, and cross finial to lid. Inscribed 'Congregational Church CHESHAM Pastor Revd C.N. Barham June 1897'. London 1897, maker 'J.N.M.'. H 10¾.　　　[26]

(11) GREAT HORWOOD (Congregational). *Cups*: pair, base metal, plain bowl with centre band on moulded stem and base. H 6⅛, D 3½. *Flagon*: domed lid with finial, double-curved handle, same material and date. Early 19th-century. H 11¾.　　　[37]

(12) HADDENHAM (Baptist). *Cups*: two (i) (Plate 15C) bowl with everted rim, short upstand at base and two barbed handles. Upper band of cable moulding between handles, lower third gadrooned. Circular cartouche, with scrolled surround and winged cherub's head above, bearing secondary inscription '*HBC | 1811*'. London 1714, maker Nathaniel Lock. H 4½, D 5, W 7½. (ii) pewter, tapered bowl with moulded rim, short rounded stem and base. Probably 18th-century. H 5, D 3⅜. *Plate*: pewter. Inscribed 'F over I N' on rim. Touch and 'hall-marks' of Henry Hammerton of London (C.2105), early 18th-century. D 9⅜.　　　[40]

(13) HANSLOPE, Long Street (Baptist). *Cup and two plates*: base metal by James Dixon and Sons, with

scratched inscription 'Long Street Hanslope [Baptist Chappele] 1845'. [46]

(14) WINSLOW, Keach's Meeting-house (Baptist). *Cup*: base metal, plain bowl on moulded stem and base. Early 19th-century. H 6, D 3⅝. [96]

CAMBRIDGESHIRE

(15) CAMBRIDGE, St Andrew's Street (Baptist). *Cups*: pair, S-shaped sides with two handles on shaped stem and base. Inscribed 'A token of Regard and Christian Affection to the Church of Christ Meeting in St. Andrews St. Cambridge under the Pastoral Care of the Revd. T. C. Edmonds A.D.1819'. London 1819, makers Thomas Wallis & Jonathan Hyde. H 8. (See also (19) below) [10]

(16) CAMBRIDGE, 'Emmanuel', Trumpington Street (Congregational/URC). *Cups*: four (i) moulded rim, gadrooning to lower third of bowl, on moulded gadrooned base, pair of barbed handles with beaded upper surface. Inscribed 'C over W S' and secondary inscription 'Given by Mrs S. Ewens 1756'. London 1698, maker John Boddington of Foster Lane. H 4½, D 5⅛. (ii) (Plate 15A) everted rim, upper band of cable moulding, lower third gadrooned, on moulded and gadrooned base, two hollow handles with thumb rests. Oval cartouche with scrolled surround and monogram of three interlaced initials, possibly 'HGS', secondary inscription at back 'Given by Mr. J. Audley 1816', and on underside initials 'E. A.'. London 1705, maker John Cory. H 4½, D 4¾, W 8. (iii) as last but only slight upstand at base, and pair of solid barbed handles. Cartouche inscribed 'S over P F' and secondary inscription at back 'Given by Mrs. F. Jennings 1816'. London 1711, maker possibly Timothy Ley. H 4, D 4¾, W 7½. (iv) generally as ii but with vertical gadrooning on bowl and no cartouche, inside gilt. Inscribed 'PRESENTED TO EMMANUEL CHURCH CAMBRIDGE BY MR WILLIAM BOND 1889'. London 1889, maker CB. H 4½, D 4¾, W 8½. *Flagon*: bulbous body, domed lid, moulded base, spout and hollow handle. Inscribed 'Given by Mr. C. Rutherford 1816'. London 1816, makers Alice & George Burrows. H 9¼. [A silver *baptismal basin*, given by Thomas Borrett in 1829, reported by Atkinson (1897) and in *CHST* IV (1909–10) 183–203, is not now in the possession of the church] [16]

(17) FOWLMERE (Congregational/URC). *Cups*: pair, pewter, straight-sided bowl with moulded rim, band at base of handles, moulded base and pair of double-curved handles. Mark of lion passant repeated thrice, early 19th-century. H 4¼, D 3⅜, W 7½. *Plates*: pair,

pewter. Touch and 'hall-marks' of Samuel Cocks (C.1004), early 19th-century. D 9⅝. [40]

(18) ISLEHAM, Pound Lane (Baptist). *Cups*: two (i) plain rounded bowl on short moulded base, two barbed handles. Inscribed on base 'G over T K'. London, date letter indistinct, ?1764 or 1766. H 2⅝, D 3¼, W 5. (ii) similar design and size as last but with moulded rim and slightly taller base. London 1840, makers John & Henry Lias. *Flagon*: with long inscription recording its donation by William Suberton of Osset in 1893. Sheffield 1894, maker 'W D & S'. H 9. *Plates*: pair, pewter. Touch of Thomas or John Major[s] of London (C.3057–8), early 18th-century. D 9¼. [54]

(19) TEVERSHAM (Baptist). *Cup*: plain bowl with two handles and short base. Inscribed 'Presented to Teversham Baptist Church by St Andrews Street Church, Cambridge, April 18th 1921'. London 1720, maker Edward Gibbon. [89]

CHESHIRE

(20) ALTRINCHAM (Unitarian). *Cups*: pair, plain bowl with everted rim on stem with moulded band and base. Inscribed in black letter '**Altrincham Chapel**'. London 1815, maker William Bateman, senior. H 8, D 3⅞. *Plate*: same description, date and maker as last. D 10. *Flagon*: London 1869, maker 'HW'. [4]

(21) APPLETON, Hill Cliff (Baptist). *Cups*: pair of pewter mugs, single handle. Possibly 18th century. H 3¾, D 4¼. *Plates*: four (i–ii) pewter. Touch of John or Samuel Duncumb (C.1465–6), 18th-century. D 9¾. (iii–iv) pewter. Touch of Samuel Duncumb (C.1466), late 18th-century. D 10¼. [8]

(22) CHESTER, Matthew Henry's Chapel (Presbyterian/Unitarian). *Cups*: two (i) bowl with upper band of cable moulding and gadrooning to lower third, small upstand at base, two handles. Oval cartouche in scrolled surround inscribed 'MH' for Matthew Henry (minister 1687–1712). London 1703, maker William Andrews. H 3⅞, D 4⅞, W 7¼. (ii) similar design to last but with winged cherub's head above cartouche. Inscribed in cartouche '*The Gift of Mrs* HANNAH STATHAM *to the Trustees of the* CHAPPEL *in* CHESTER *to be used at the* LORD'S SUPPER 1732'. London 1723, maker Thomas Tearle. H 4⅞, D 5⅜, W 8½. *Flagons*: two, pewter, almost alike, no spout, spreading base. (i) Scratched 'Holby' on base. 'Hall-marks' include letter 'C'. H 13. (ii) 'Hall-marks' include 'H.I.'. H 12¾. *Plates*: two, pewter. 'Hall-marks' include initials 'T B', touch of crowned rose 'FROM LONDON'.

[Evans (1897, pp 44–5) also records the following unlocated items *Cups*: two, plain bowl with everted rim, hollow stem with band, moulded base. Inscribed 'The Legacy of Mrs Mary Bevan to the Presbyterian Congregation in Chester 1745'. London 1745. H 8½. (Also illustrated in Jones (1905–6), Pl.XXI, with incorrect caption)] [24]

(23) DUKINFIELD, Old Chapel (Presbyterian/Unitarian). *Cups*: two (i) (Plate 12A) plain bowl with slight moulded base and two barbed handles. Inscribed '*Donum, Samuelis Angier: VDM; Ecclesiae apud Dukinfield 1713*'. London 1690, maker 'SH linked'. H 4¼, D 4⅝, W 7½. (ii) similar to last but with thicker handles. Inscribed '*Jane Leech Hunc Calicem Ecclesiæ Apud Dukinfield dono Dedit A.D.1858*'. Sheffield 1858, makers Hawksworth, Eyre and Co. *Plates*: pair. Inscribed (i) '*In memoriam Nancy Lees hanc patinam Ecclesiæ apud Dukinfield ad cultum unius Dei consecratæ Maria Aspland Dono Dedit A.D. 1858*'. D 9¼. (ii) as above but '*In memoriam Mariae Bayley, Henricus Bayley, dono*'. Both Sheffield 1858. [40]

(24) GREAT WARFORD (Baptist). [Three pewter vessels, a *cup* with stem and foot, H approx. 7, another *cup* with two handles, H approx. 6, and a *plate*, D approx. 10, are understood to be in the care of Macclesfield Museums.] [47]

(25) HALE, Hale Barns (Presbyterian/Unitarian). *Cups*: four (i–ii) pair, tapered bowl on tall stem with centre band and moulded base. Inscribed 'Hale Chapel 1801', '*THE GIFT* of Mr Jno. Worthington', and around outer edge of base 'the Gift of Mr John Worthington of Altrincham'. London 1800, makers Peter, Ann & William Bateman. H 9, D 3⅞. (iii–iv) pair, pewter, plain bowl with everted rim, short moulded base and pair of double-curved handles. 'Hall-marks' possibly of W. Baldwin (C.213), early 18th-century. H 4, D 4¼, W 6¾. *Plates*: two. (i) Inscribed underneath 'HALE CHAPEL 1804 The GIFT of Mr Isaac Worthington'. London 1803, maker 'HN'. (ii) pewter. Touch and 'hall-marks' of — Fly (C.1703–4). D 13⅜. [49]

(26) KNUTSFORD, Brook Street (Presbyterian/Unitarian). *Cup*: plain bowl with everted rim, short upstand at base and two barbed handles. Inscribed on base 'B over E M'. London 1694, maker 'R pellet below' for ?Alexander Roode. H 3¼, D 3¾. *Plates*: two, pewter. Touch of Fly & Thompson (C.1703), mid-18th-century. D 9½. [60]

(27) LYMM, Higher Lane (Baptist). *Cup*: plated, shaped bowl, stem and base, two handles. Inscribed 'Baptist Chapel Lymm | Feb.y 1854'. [67]

(28) MACCLESFIELD, King Edward Street (Presbyterian/Unitarian). *Cups*: pair, plain bowl with everted rim, hollow stem with centre band and moulded base. Inscribed (i) '*The Gift of John Broadhurst of Hudsfield 1728*'; (ii) '*Ex Dono Thomae Culcheth V.D.M. 1728*'. London 1727, maker 'WP in shield'. H 8, D 4. *Plates*: three (i–ii) pair. Engraved with sunburst and inscribed 'THE GIFT OF SARAH WIDOW OF THE LATE JOHN BROCKLEHURST ESQRE. OF JORDAN-GATE MACCLESFIELD 1841'. London 1840, makers Edward, Edward jnr., John & William Barnard. D 10. (iii) with central foot. Same inscription, date and makers as last. H 2, D 8½. *Baptismal basin*: pewter, with 2¼ in. wide rim. Stamped initials include 'TH in shields', and touch of pomegranate between palm branches, 18th-century. H 2, D 13⅜. [71]

(29) SPURSTOW (Primitive Methodist). *Cup*: lustreware, silvered face, inside gilt, plain bowl with moulded stem and base. 19th-century. H 5½, D 4¼. [126]

(30) STOCKPORT, Stockport Road, formerly St Petersgate (Presbyterian/Unitarian). *Cups*: pair, plain bowl with everted rim on baluster stem and wide moulded base. London 1753, makers William Shaw & William Priest. H 8⅞, D 3⅞. *Plates*: pair, pewter. London label and touch of three leopards' heads in oval frame (C.6046), late 18th-century. D 9¾. *Alms-dish* (or *Baptismal basin*): pewter. Touch as on plates. H 1⅝, D 10½. [128]

(31) TINTWISTLE (Congregational). *Cups*: four, with everted rim, reeded centre band, on short stem with moulded base, pair of hollow handles. Inscribed 'TINTWISTLE CHAPEL'. H 6¼, D 3⅜, W 7. (i–ii) London 1803, maker Thomas Ollivant overstamped with mark of Peter & William Bateman. (iii) Inscribed on one handle 'I:A'. London 1807, makers Peter & William Bateman. (iv) London 1809, makers Peter & William Bateman. [134]

CORNWALL

(32) MORVAH (Wesleyan Methodist). *Cup*: lustreware, silvered face, inside gilt, tapered bowl with everted rim, short stem and base. Early 19th-century. H 3¾, D 3½. [In private possession 1969] [104]

(33) ST AGNES, Blackwater (Wesleyan Methodist). *Cups*: pair, lustreware, silvered face, inside gilt, rounded bowl enriched with frosted foliage, stem with rounded knop and base. Early 19th-century. H 5¾, D 3¼. [135]

CUMBERLAND

(34) BEWCASTLE (Presbyterian/URC). *Cups*: pair, plain bowl with everted rim, tall moulded stem and base. Inscribed 'W.M LAUDER BEAUCASTLE 1789'.

Late 18th-century. H 9¼, D 5. *Flagon*: (Plate 25A) pewter, tapered body, moulded rim, wide central band, moulded base, flat lid with thumb rest and later finial, thin S-shaped handle, spout. Inscription as on last. Touch, inside base, a ship in full sail and motto 'SUCCESS TO Ye BRITISH COLONIES S MAXWELL', for Stephen Maxwell of Glasgow (C.3153), late 18th-century. H 10¼ (to finial), 8⅜ (to rim). *Plate*: pewter. Inscribed 'R over I M' on rim. No marks. D 16¾. [All these now in URCHS collection]   [12]

(35) BRAMPTON (Presbyterian/URC). *Cups*: four, base metal (i–iii) tulip-shaped bowl, plain stem and rounded base. Inscribed 'Brampton 1856'. H 6¼, D 3. (iv) petal-shaped body, stem and invected octagonal base. Late 19th-century. H 9½, D 4¼. *Flagons*: two, base metal. (i) Inscribed as on cups i–iii. H 10¾. (ii) Inscribed 'Presented to the Presbyterian Church Brampton by a few friends and well wishers 14th December 1883'. H 15. *Plates*: pair, base metal, contemporary with cups i–iii. D 10.   [20]

[Also here is a base metal set of a two-handled *cup*, two *plates* and two deep dishes from the former Congregational chapel, 19th-century. [19]]

(36) CARLISLE, Lowther Street (Congregational). *Cups*: three, Sheffield plate (i–ii) pair, tapered bowl on plain stem and moulded base. Inscribed below swag 'LUKE.XXII.&XX. This cup *is* the new testament in my blood, which is shed for you.'. Late 18th-century. H 8, D 4. (iii) plain bowl with everted rim, stem with triple moulded band, moulded base. Mid-19th-century. H 8½, D 3⅞.   [30]

(37) MARYPORT (Presbyterian/URC). *Cups*: pair, Sheffield plate, plain bowl with moulded rim, stem with centre band, moulded base closed below by circular wooden plate. Inscribed '*Maryport Presbytn. Society 1776*'. Late 18th-century. H 6½, D 4. *Flagons*: two (i) Sheffield plate, body with reeded band, moulded base closed as cups, handle and domed lid, no spout. Late 18th-century. H 7¾. (ii) base metal, cylindrical body with moulded rim, reeded centre band, moulded base, domed lid, spout, and thick hollow handle. Maker's mark 'I*VICKERS', early 19th-century. H 12⅛. Plate: pewter. Inscribed on rim 'IG'. Touch illegible. D 15. [All these now in URCHS collection]   [87]

(38) WHITEHAVEN, James Street (Presbyterian/URC). *Cups*: (Plate 11B) pair, pewter, bowl with slightly concave sides and moulded lower band, on thick baluster stem and moulded base. Inscribed 'PRESBYTERIAN COMMUNITY OF WHITEHAVEN'.

Mid-18th-century. H 8¼–8¾, D 5. [All these now in URCHS collection]   [112]

DERBYSHIRE

(39) BELPER, Field Row (Presbyterian/Unitarian). *Cups*: pair, Sheffield plate, plain bowl on stem and base. Mark, an orb, 19th-century. H 8. *Plates*: pair, plated. D 7½.   [13]

(40) BOLSOVER, Old Meeting-house (Presbyterian/Congregational). *Cup*: Sheffield plate with silver rim to edge and base, bowl with swept stem and moulded base, two handles rising high above rim. Early 19th-century. H 7¾ (top of handles) 6⅝ (rim), D 4⅛, W 7¾. *Plates*: pair, pewter. Each stamped with owner's initials 'RS'. Touch of Edward Leapidge of London, post-1728 (C.2894). D 9⅝.   [17]

(41) CHESTERFIELD, Elder Yard (Presbyterian/Unitarian). *Cups*: pair, plain bowl with everted rim, hollow stem with band, moulded base. London 1709, maker Humphrey Payne. H 6⅞, D 4. [Evans (1897) 46, also lists two pewter *plates* marked 'COMMUNION'] [39]

(42) CHINLEY, BUXWORTH AND BROWNSIDE, Chinley Chapel (Congregational). *Cup*: (Plate 7B) tapered bowl, baluster stem, wide base. London 1637, maker's mark probably 'a pillar between GS' (Jackson (1989) 117). H 6⅞, D 4. *Plates*: pair, pewter. Touch includes 'the golden fleece' (cf. C.1547, 4179, 4593), name not identified. D 9¼.   [43]

(43) DERBY, Friar Gate (Presbyterian/Unitarian). *Cups*: pair, plain bowl with short upstand at base, two handles. Inscribed 'K✳W'. London 1724, maker John Wisdome. H 4⅛. D 4½, W 7¼. *Plates*: four, pewter. Inscribed 'D over E A' on rim. All with 'London' label and one with touch of William Cooke of Bristol and Gloucester (C.1095). D 8½. [Evans (1897) also lists a '*tankard* or *flagon*' with straight sides, flat lid with thumb rest and one handle, engraved with a shield or lozenge-of-arms and with a secondary inscription beneath: 'THE GIFT OF THE HONOURABLE MRS. E. ALSOP TO THE CONGREGATION OF PROTESTANT DISSENTERS IN DERBY. OB. MARCH 1, 1712/13. ÆT.94'. London 1685. H 5¾, D 5 (at base), weight 24 oz. 18 dwt. Missing since *c*.1940, illustrated by Evans (1897) facing page 68 and in Jones (1905–6) Pl.XI]   [51]

(44) DUFFIELD (Presbyterian/Unitarian). Congregation dissolved *c*.1867 and plate transferred to Friar Gate Chapel, Derby. *Cups*: two (i) plain bowl, moulded base, two handles. Inscribed 'THE GIFT OF THE REPRESENTATIVES OF THE LATE HENRY COAPE ESQ^R TO THE CONGREGATION OF

PROTESTANT DISSENTERS AT DUFFIELD 20TH AUGUST 1778' and on underside 'E∗H'. London 1726, maker ?John Wisdome. H 3¾, D 3⅞, W 6½. (ii) plain bowl, short upstand at base, two handles. Inscription and initials as last. London 1731, maker Gabriel Sleath. H 3⅝, D 4⅛, W 7. [Evans (1897) 68–9, also lists *Plates*: pair, inscribed as above but without initials. London 1702. D 9½. Missing] [51]

(45) HAYFIELD (Methodist). *Cups*: pair, Britannia metal, plain bowl on flared stem and base. Maker I.Vickers, early 19th-century. H 7¼. *Plate*: with foot, same maker. [85]

(46) OCKBROOK (Moravian). *Cup*: Sheffield plate, bowl with everted rim and moulded band, on flared base; two handles and cover. Initials 'OC' on base. H 7⅛, D 4½, W 8½. [120]

DEVONSHIRE

(47) BIDEFORD, Great Meeting (Presbyterian/Congregational/URC). *Cups*: (Plate 5B) four (i) tapered bowl, baluster stem, flat base. Inscribed 'S over D W / 1649' and secondary inscription '*The Gift of Sarah Jones Widow to the Great Meeting House in BIDEFORD 1747*' above scrolls and winged cherub's head. London 1634, maker 'WC, heart below'. H 7½, D 3¾. (ii) similar to last but bowl slightly less tapered. Inscribed below rim 'KC/RT'. London 1637, maker 'WC, heart below'. H 7½, D 4. (iii) plain bowl with everted rim, baluster stem, flat base. Inscribed 'B over T T'. London 1656, maker 'RN between mullets' for ?Richard Neale. H 5¾, D 3½. (iv) similar to last but with more conical base. Inscribed below rim 'S over TS / 1679' and secondary inscription '*This Cup given by Mary Gunion 1737 To the Use of the Meeting for Ever*'. Bideford *c*.1675, maker John Peard (Jackson (1989) 313). H 6⅜, D 3½. *Flagon*: plated base metal with silver insert, tapered body, moulded base, band below handle, leaf finial on lid. Inscribed 'Presented by THOMAS SPENCER for the use of the Independent Church BIDEFORD 1845'. H 14. *Plates*: pair, similar material and inscription as last. D 8. [10]

(48) CREDITON TOWN, Bowden Hill, Crediton (Presbyterian/Unitarian). Meeting-house closed *c*.1965 and plate transferred to Horsham, Sussex (see (269) below). *Cup*: (Plate 29B) inside gilt, octagonal bowl with everted rim, stem with knop, octagonal base, bowl enriched with Gothic arcading and 'IHS' in sunburst. Inscribed below base 'Joanna Madge to Bowden Hill Chapel 1861'. London 1840, makers Joseph and John Angel. H 8, D (between parallel sides) 4⅛. [56]

(49) CULLOMPTON, Pound Square (Presbyterian/ Unitarian). *Cup*: mug with moulded rim and base, hollow handle. Inscribed on handle 'PB/1693' and secondary inscription on bowl 'Bequeathed by Frances Brown July 28th, 1832 to the Members of the Unitarian Congregation, Cullompton To be used solely for administering the Lords Supper'. London 1693, maker 'HB between two mullets in oval'. H 4⅜, D 3⅝, W 6. *Plates*: two, pewter. (i) Inscribed on base 'F over I E'. Touch of lion rampant holding a ?key, in arched frame with two twisted columns, not identified; London label. D 9¾. (ii) Inscribed 'P over R E' twice. Touch 'GM 1686' in circle, not identified. D 9¼. [61]

(50) DARTMOUTH (Presbyterian/Congregational/ URC). *Cups*: pair of mugs with shaped sides, moulded base, one handle. Inscribed 'Given to the use of the church of the Presbytⁿ Denomin^o in Dartm^o 1738'. London 1737, maker Richard Bayley. H 4⅝, D 3¼, W 5⅛. (For a cup associated with John Flavell *see* Plymouth (58) below) [67]

(51) EXETER, George's Meeting, formerly James's Meeting (Presbyterian/Unitarian). *Cups*: (Plate 6A) two (i) tapered bowl, baluster stem and wide base. Inscribed below rim 'IW', secondary inscription 'No.1 James's Meeting' and on base '9oz 17'. London 1636, maker illegible. H 7⅛. D 3⅞. (ii) similar to last but more angular bowl. Inscribed below rim 'M over I M / 166i', secondary inscription 'No.2 James's Meeting' and on base '12oz 17'. London 1660, maker 'WM mullet below'. H 6¾, D 4⅛. *Plates*: two (i) wide rim. Centre engraved with bunched drapery and inscribed 'No:1 The Gift of *John Vowler Esq To the Society at James's Meeting* Exon *March 25th, 1746*'. London 1705, maker's initials illegible, above a mullet. D 9⅝. (ii) (Plate 26B) similar pattern, size and inscription to last except 'No:2 ... '. London 1712, maker Richard Green. [75]

(52) EXETER, South Street (Baptist). *Cups*: pair, everted rim, moulded band and base, two double-curved handles. Each inscribed on outer edge of one handle '*Baptist Meeting Exon*'. Exeter 1725, maker John Elston jun. (a member of this church). [Now in Royal Albert Memorial Museum and Art Gallery, Queen Street, Exeter] [78]

(53) EXMOUTH, Point-in-View (Congregational). [*Bowl*: shallow dish, heavily embossed, with two handles and three short claw feet, separate cover similarly footed and decorated. Inscribed 'Ex Dono I.P., 1677'. London, 1679, maker 'A.R. mullet below'. W 12. Given 1812 by the Misses Parminter for Communion use, sold 1928, unlocated. Photograph in vestry] [84]

(54) HONITON, Old Meeting (General Baptist/Unitarian). Plated set comprising two-handled *cup* with shaped body and moulded base, two square *plates* with bracket-shaped sides and shallow bowl with handle, possibly mid-19th-century. All with later inscription 'This piece of Communion plate formerly belonged to the Old Meeting, Honiton, Devon, where it was in use for many years'. [Now at Essex Hall, London]   [98]

(55) HONITON (Congregational). *Cup*: Sheffield plate, inside gilt, beaker-shaped bowl with moulded rim and bottom band, on plain stem and reeded base. Early 19th-century. H 6⅛, D 3¼.   [98]

(56) ILFRACOMBE (Congregational/URC). *Cup*: inside gilt, plain tapered bowl with continuous stem and reeded base. London 1810, maker 'E.F'. H 6⅞, D 3½. *Flagon*: straight-sided body with lower band, lid with finial. London 1837, maker William Bateman jnr. H 9½.   [99]

(57) MORETONHAMPSTEAD, Cross Street (Presbyterian/Unitarian). *Cup*: bowl with everted rim, short upstand at base and two barbed handles, upper band of cable moulding, gadrooning to lower third and oval cartouche in scrolled surround. Inscribed 'I∗L / 1731' for John Lane whose widow gave the cup to the congregation. London 1703, maker probably John Cory. H 4⅝, D 5¼, W 7¾.   [127]

(58) PLYMOUTH, Prince's Street (Congregational). This congregation, now represented by the 'Pilgrim church' (URC), formerly possessed the following item, sold *c*. 1971 and unlocated. It is here described from the illustrated note in *CHST* III (1907–8), 153. [*Cup*: with tapered bowl, baluster stem and wide base. Inscribed '1663 / D over I F' for John Flavell, Dartmouth, ejected minister and first pastor of the Dartmouth congregation. Said to have been later given to Prince's Street church by Revd Andrew Kinsman, first pastor (1763–93), probably *c*. 1650–60]   [67]

(59) PLYMOUTH, Treville Street, now Notte Street (Independent/Presbyterian/Unitarian). *Cups*: (Plate 5A) two (i) tapered bowl, baluster stem, wide base. Secondary inscription below rim 'Bought by, & for the use of that Church in Plymouth of which Nathaniel Harding is Pastor. 1705'. London 1632, maker 'RC, pheon below'. H 6¾, D 3⅞; (ii) similar pattern to last but sides less tapered. Same inscription. London 1660 or 1662, maker 'RN, mullet and two pellets below'. H 7, D 4. *Flagon*: tall cylindrical body with cross finial. Inscribed on base '*Unitarian Chapel Plymouth Presented by Mary Anne Grant 1869*'. London 1870, maker ECB. H 12. *Plate*: with central foot. Inscribed

with monogram 'ME intertwined' and date 1710. London 1709, maker's mark indistinct, possibly Timothy Ley. H 2½, D 9⅜. [At City Museum, Tavistock Road, Plymouth]   [147]

(60) SIDMOUTH, Old Meeting (Presbyterian/Unitarian). *Cup*: bowl with everted rim, centre band, rounded stem and moulded base, two handles. London 1807, makers Peter & William Bateman. H 6, D 3⅞, W 7. *Plate*: on three short legs, ornamental sexpartite border, given 1807 by Judith Gundry (*UHST* III (1923–6) 64–5). London 1749, maker David Willaume jnr. H 1¼, D 8⅝.   [158]

(61) TAVISTOCK, Abbey Chapel (Presbyterian/Unitarian). *Cups*: (Plate 20A) two mugs of generally similar pattern, straight-sided body with two moulded bands, differently spaced, moulded rim and base, strap handle. Each inscribed below base 'M.F'. Assay marks indistinct but possibly London, late 17th-century, one with maker's initials 'PR'. H 3⅜, D 3¼.   [166]

(62) TOPSHAM, Victoria Road (Presbyterian/Unitarian). [The plate from this congregation comprising two standing *cups* with baluster stems, late 17th-century, H. 6½, and a plate with central foot, with inscribed date of 1705, was presented in 1920 to Meadville Theological College, Chicago]   [183]

DORSET

(63) BERE REGIS, Old Meeting (Presbyterian/Independent). The following may have been transferred to the seceding Congregational church in 1813 to which the donor adhered. *Cup*: Sheffield plate, shaped bowl on short rounded stem and base, two handles. Inscribed '*THE GIFT OF JOHN KING TO THE COMMUNICANT DISSENTERS OF BERE REGIS 1802*'. H 6⅞, D 4⅜, W 8½.   [7]

(64) BLANDFORD FORUM (Congregational/URC). *Cups*: pair, bowl with slightly everted rim, slight upstand at base and two barbed handles, upper band of cable moulding, gadrooning to lower third, circular cartouche with surround of leaf ornament passing below cable moulding. Inscribed 'BMH' for Blandford Meeting House. London 1714, maker Richard Green. H 3⅞, D 4¾, W 7–7⅛. *Flagon*: plated, body with reeded band, moulded base, domed lid. Mid-19th-century. H 12¼.   [9]

(65) BRIDPORT, East Street (Presbyterian/Unitarian). *Cups*: pair, plain bowl with everted rim, moulded base, two hollow handles. Inscribed below rim 'h / C'. London 1726, maker Matthew Lofthouse, mark repeated on base and handles. H 4¼, D 4⅛, W 7. *Plates*: pair, pewter, silvered. Inscribed 'W over O A'.

Touch of Hale & Sons of Bristol, with false London mark (C.2070), late 19th-century. D 9¼. [11]

(66) HAMPRESTON, Longham (Congregational/URC). Base metal set by James Dixon & Sons, early 19th-century, comprising *cups*: two, plain bowl on stem with knop, moulded base, H 8⅛, D 4; *flagon*: with domed lid, H 13½; *plates*: two, D 10. [38]

(67) POOLE, Old Meeting (Presbyterian/Unitarian). [*Cups*: 'two silver cups or muggs' given by Mrs Joan Green, 1722, were reported (Evans (1897) 201–2) to be then in possession of Skinner Street congregation. Unlocated] [68]

(68) POOLE, Skinner Street (Congregational/URC). *Cups*: four, plain bowl with everted rim, moulded base, two handles. Inscribed '*Independent | Meeting | Skinner Street | Poole | 1810*'. London 1810, makers Rebecca Emes & Edward Barnard. H 4⅞, D 4⅜. *Flagons*: pair, Sheffield plate, tapered body with hinged lid, handle, spout, and moulded base. Inscribed 'PRESENTED | by the | Female Members | of the | Church of Christ | assembling in the | Independent Meeting House | POOLE | 1836'. H 12. *Plates*: four, Sheffield plate, with gadrooned rim. Inscribed 'Independent | MEETING | Skinner Street | POOLE | 1836'. D 10⅛. [69]

(69) SHAFTESBURY (Congregational/URC). *Cups*: pair, plain bowl with everted rim, two handles, moulded base. Bowl inscribed 'Sacramental | 1752' in scrolled surround. London 1751, maker John Swift. H 4½, D 3⅞. [81]

(70) SHERBORNE (Congregational/URC). *Cups*: pair, bowl with everted rim, two strap handles, moulded base. Bowl engraved on one face with cartouche of arms above inscription 'MK 1723' and on other face 'The Gift of Mary Kelsby to the Meeting of Sherborne for the use of the Sacrament'. London 1723, maker Gabriel Sleath. H 5½, D 5, W 8¼. *Plates*: six, pewter dated 1723, later silver plating. [85]

(71) WAREHAM (Presbyterian/Congregational/URC). [*Cup*: 'a silver tankard ... known as "Parson Clark's cup"' possibly used for communion by William Clark, first minister (1670–1722) is referred to by Densham and Ogle (1899) 338. Missing, believed stolen *c.* 1939–45] (See also (72) below) [101]

(72) WAREHAM (Unitarian). *Cups*: (Plate 20B) pair of mugs, tapered bowl with moulded rim, pair of moulded bands and moulded base, single handle with beaded band on face. London 1704, maker John Cory. H 4⅝, D 4¾ [stolen from Essex Hall, London, 1971]. *Plates*: pair, pewter. Inscribed on base 'B over RE'. Touch of Ash & Hutton of Bristol, with false London

label (C.118), *c.* 1760. D 9¼. (These items are claimed to have belonged to the foregoing congregation (71) before the Unitarians seceded in 1828). [103]

DURHAM

(73) DURHAM, Claypath (Presbyterian/Congregational/URC). *Cups*: (Plate 7D) pair, tapered bowl on baluster stem and flared base, bowl and base are engraved with foliage and retain slight traces of former gilding, shield-of-arms on bowl, a chevron between three antelopes' heads couped, with helm, mantling and crest of antelope's head. Band below rim inscribed '*The Property of the Dissenting Meeting, Durham, The Rev^d J:Hart Min^r 1775*'. London 1647, maker 'WT'. H 5⅜, D 3⅜. [13]

(74) SUNDERLAND, Malings Rigg (Presbyterian). *Cup*: formerly one of a pair, pewter, plain straight-sided bowl, moulded rim, short stem, domical base, two hollow handles with heart-shaped terminals. Bowl engraved with large oval enclosing inscription '⁎ | THIS CUP, | *is the Gift of the Trustees of* | MALINGS *Rigg Chapell,* | *To the Congregation,* | *June 10th 1815*'. H 6½, D 4¼, W 8¼. *Flagon*: one, pewter, tapered body, moulded rim, base and lower band, reeded band in upper third, spout, double-curved handle, domed lid with urn finial. Inscribed below spout '*The Property of the* | DISSENTING CONGREGATION OF | *Malings Ridge,* | SUNDERLAND, | DURHAM. | 1797', also on side '*The Gift of ANN-GOWEN,* | *to* | *this Congregation* | *Anno Domi: 1797*'. H 11¾ overall, 8⅞ to rim. [In URCHS Collection] [57]

(75) SUNDERLAND, North Wearmouth (Presbyterian). *Cups*: four, Britannia metal, plain bowl with moulded base and two reeded strap handles. Inscribed on two faces '*Scotch Church*' and '*No . . Wearmouth* | 1805*'. One with touch of I.Vickers. H 6¼, D 4¼, W 7⅞. [In URCHS Collection]

(76) SUNDERLAND, Robinson's Lane (Presbyterian). *Flagon*: pewter, plain body with moulded rim and base, domed lid with finial and thumb rest, S-shaped handle, no spout. Body inscribed 'MEETING HOUSE IN | ROBINSON'S LANE | *SUNDERLAND* | 1766'. H 14⅜ overall, 10¾ to rim. [In URCHS collection] [57]

(77) WHICKHAM, Swalwell (Presbyterian/URC). *Cups*: pair, base metal, tapered body, stem, wide base. Late 18th-century. H 7¾, D 3¾. *Flagon*: base metal, spout, domed lid, handle. James Dixon & Sons. H 12. *Plates*: four, pewter (i–ii) pair. Inscribed on rim 'WOOD SIDE MEETING'. Touch of G. Lowes, *c.* 1720–50. D 9¼. (iii–iv) pair. Inscribed 'SWALWELL MEETING'. Late 18th-century. D 9½. [62]

ESSEX

(78) ABBESS BEAUCHAMP AND BERNERS RODING, Abbess Roding (Presbyterian/Congregational). *Cups*: pair, plain bowl with everted rim and slight upstand at base, pair of hollow handles with thumb rests. Face of bowl inscribed '*This belongs to ye Desenting : Meeting | at Abbots Rooding | John Cooke | Pastor | 1747*'. London 1747, maker Thomas Whipham. H 3¾, D 4, W 7¼. [In Colchester Museum]   [1]

(79) COLCHESTER, Lion Walk (Congregational/URC). *Cups*: (Plate 4B, C) set of four beakers, plain straight-sided bowl with everted rim and moulded base. Inscribed on underside of base '*Colchester | Moor Lane Meeting | ye Church's Property | ye Revd Mr E. Cornell | Pastor. | 1755*'. London 1754, maker Walter Brind. H 5½–5⅝, D 3¼. *Plates*: six, pewter with later plating. (i–iv) Stamped 'U G crowned'. Touch of John Watts of London (C.4991) with crowned rose and London label, mid-18th-century. D 9¾. (v–vi) Stamped 'I M E crowned'. Touch of Jonathan Cotton of London (C.1137–8), mid-18th-century. D 9¾.   [27]

(80) COLCHESTER, St Helens Lane (Former Presbyterian). *Cups*: two, of similar pattern, plain bowl with everted rim on hollow stem with moulded band and base. (i) Inscribed '*The Gift of Robert Cockly to that Church of wch Mr Dan^ll Gilson | is present Pastor. Colchester 1715 – *'. London, date indistinct, possibly pre-1679, maker 'W / W + . .'. (ii) Inscribed as last but dated 1717 and with slight variation in punctuation. London 1716, maker Humphrey Payne. H 8½, D 4⅝. [Later property of the Congregational Church in Stockwell Street, but from 1914 part of Colchester Civic Plate]   [28]

(81) FORDHAM (Countess of Huntingdon's). *Baptismal basin*: (Plate 27C) base metal, circular on moulded base. Late 18th-century. H 6½, W 10½.   [41]

(82) HARLOW, Potter Street (Baptist). *Cups*: pair, plain bowl with shaped sides, everted and moulded rim, moulded base, two double-curved handles. Inscription below base '*Potters Street Meeting 1760*'. London 1760, makers William Shaw & William Priest. H 4⅛, D 3⅝, W 6¼. *Plates*: five (i–iii), three, silver plate on base metal, rounded rim. Inscribed on underside as last. Possibly 18th-century. D 9. (iv–v) pair, electroplate by 'J D & S', late 19th-century or after. D 10½.   [61]

(83) LITTLE BADDOW (Congregational/URC). *Cups*: two (i) plain bowl with everted rim, moulded base, two double-curved handles with leaf ornament above. Bowl inscribed on two sides '*E. Jones, Pastor*', '*This belongs to Little Baddow | Meeting in Essex*

1766'. London 1766, makers Thomas Whipham & Charles Wright of Ave Maria Lane, London. H 6, D 4⅝, W 8⅜. (ii) rounded tapering bowl on swept stem and base, bowl enriched with swag and leaf ornament and base with border of the last. Bowl inscribed '*STEPHEN MORELL | PASTOR. | 1824*'. London 1774, maker John Carter. H 6, D 3¾. *Flagon*: electroplate, with handle, spout, domed lid. Marked 'A B ✻ S', late 19th-century. H 11.   [73]

GLOUCESTERSHIRE

(84) BRISTOL, Pithay, later Old King Street (Baptist). *Cup*: one, pewter, plain bowl, short rounded stem on moulded base, two handles. Uninscribed. 18th-century. H 7, D 4⅝, W 8½. *Flagon*: pewter, baluster-shaped body on bell foot, handle, domed lid, spout. Uninscribed. 18th-century. H 15¼. *Plate*: pewter, on single moulded foot. Touch of Bush & Perkins of Bristol and Bitton, Glos., with false London label (C.740), late 18th-century. H 4½, D 11¾. [At Bristol Baptist College]   [15]

(85) BRISTOL, Lewin's Mead (Presbyterian/Unitarian). *Cups*: four, bowl with everted rim, moulded centre band, moulded foot, two handles. Inscribed around lower part of bowl '*The Gift of M:W. to ye Congregation at Lewins-Mead, Bristol, 1728.*' (one cup has spelling '*Lewens*'). London 1727, maker 'WP mullet below' for William Paradise. H 4½, D 4⅛, W 7¼. *Plates*: four. One only is inscribed '*The Gift of Mr William Beverstone to the Congregation in Lewingsmead 1728*'. London 1727, makers mark illegible. *Flagon*: tapered body, moulded base, handle, domed lid with foliated finial, spout. Engraved with cartouche of palm branches enclosing a cross and inscription 'DO THIS IN REMEMBRANCE OF ME', base inscribed 'Presented by the Ladies of the Lewins Mead Congregation in the 22nd year of the Ministry of the Revd. R. C. Jones, December, 1863'. London 1863, maker Martin Hall & Co. of Sheffield. H 14. (Prior to the purchase of this flagon the church used a set of six *Decanters* of dark green Bristol glass, two only of which remain, with banded and faceted necks. H 8⅞, W at base 4½.)   [32]

(86) CAM, Upper Cam (Congregational). *Plates*: two, pewter (i) (Plate 26E) broad rim, overall engraving including large central fleur-de-luce. Inscription around rim 'THE GIFTE IS SMALE ✻ THE LOVE IS ALL Lydia Purnel 1673'. Touch 'I P' (C.5835). D 9¾. (ii) Owners initials below, 'D over I E' individually crowned. Touch of Stephen Cox (C.1189), mid-18th-century. D 9¼.   [33]

(87) CIRENCESTER, Gosditch Street (Presbyterian/Unitarian). *Cup*: bowl with everted rim, straight sides, moulded base and band between two hollow handles. Engraved on face with rococo cartouche inscribed 'B | GURNEE' and owner's initials on handles 'E ＊ G' ,'I ＊ G'. London 1732, maker William Darker. H 5⅜, D 4⅝, W 8⅛. *Plates*: two, pewter. Touch of Duncumb. D 9⅝.

[59]

(88) GLOUCESTER, Barton Street (Presbyterian & Independent/Unitarian). [*Cups*: four mugs, straight sides, moulded rim, reeded upper band and similar at base, hollow handle. Inscription, perhaps secondary, '*Independent Meeting | GLOUCESTER*'. London 1702, maker John Sutton. H approx. 4. These were bequeathed by the Revd John Forbes in 1712 but reputedly retained by Independent seceders in 1715 and sold 1923. Now reported (Ann Eatwell) to be in Gloucester Museum]

[75, 76]

(89) STOW-ON-THE-WOLD (Baptist). *Cups*: (Plate 20D) pair of mugs with slightly tapered barrel-shaped bodies, moulded at top and bottom and with intermediate band, single moulded strap handle. Inscription '*The Gift of Mrs Marg^t Freeman of | Guiting (for ye use of the Sacrament) | to ye Baptist Church Meeting | Near Morton & Stow*'. London 1709, maker 'CO' for ?George Cox. H 3⅛, D 2⅝, W 3⅝. *Plates*: pair, pewter, touch of John Shorey (C.4623), early 18th-century. D 9⅛.

[134]

(90) ULEY, Union Chapel (Congregational). *Cups*: pair, plain rounded bowl on swept stem and reeded base. Inscribed below rim '*The Gift of James Uley Harris Esq. to the Union Chapel, 1790 +* '. London 1792, maker Charles Chesterman. H 6⅛, D 3¼. *Flagon*: plated base metal, barrel-shaped body, domed lid, spout, S-shaped handle, moulded base. Inscribed below spout 'Presented by | ELIZABETH PARADISE, *Of Dursley* | To WHITE COURT CHAPEL, | Uley | 1868'. Maker 'J & JW'. H 10⅝. *Plates*: six (i–ii) plated base metal. D 9. (iii–vi) pewter. Touch of Duncumb. D 9–9½. [All items, except the pewter plates, are now in Stroud Museum]

[154]

(91) WINTERBOURNE, Frenchay (Presbyterian/Unitarian). *Cup*: plain bowl with moulded rim, intermediate band and moulded base, two handles with leaf ornament above. Inscribed on two faces '＊ S ＊ Cup, | Frenchay | 1755' and 'E : Dono | E : Garlick'. London 1728, maker 'WP'. H 4⅝, D 4, W 6¾. Plate: pewter, with single foot. Engraved with crest *lion rampant*. Touch of Robert Nicholson of London (C.3400), early 18th-century. H 3¼, D 9⅛.

[161]

GREATER LONDON

(92) CITY OF LONDON, Carter Lane Mission (Unitarian). Electroplate set of *c.*1867. Each engraved with 'IHS' in sunburst and inscribed '+ Carter Lane Mission 1867 +'. *Cups*: two, stem with knop, moulded foot. H 9⅛. *Flagon*: handle, spout, hinged lid. H 13. *Plates*: two. D 10⅛. [At Essex Hall]

(93) CITY OF LONDON, Founders' Hall, later 'Scots Church', London Wall and Canonbury (Presbyterian). *Cups*: (Plate 14A) four, bowl with slight upstand at base, two barbed handles, cable-moulded upper band and gadrooned lower third. Inscribed beneath with initials of donors (i) 'H ＊ F' for Hugh Fraser; (ii) 'I ＊ G' for John Gallasty; (iii) 'W ＊ G' for William Graham; (iv) 'W ＊ S' and 'I ＊ C' for Walter Stewart and James Campbell. London 1694, maker '*R with pellet beneath*' for ?Alexander Roode. H 4¼, D 4¼, W 7¼. (The names of the donors of the cups, given in 1694, are recorded on a list compiled in 1717 which also includes the gift 'by Mr Samuel Clayat' of '2 Salvers and 6 Pewter Plates' *PHSJ*, V (1935) 228). *Flagons*: pair, pewter, with tapered body, moulded rim, upper band, splayed base, lid with finial, thin handle, no spout. Reported (*op. cit.*) to have touch of Joseph Bowden (C.524), early 18th-century. H 15. *Plate*: pewter, inscribed on rim '*Scots Church London* Wall'. Late 18th-century. D 9¾. [All the above, given in 1916 to the Presbyterian Historical Society, are now in the Museum of London]

(94) CITY OF LONDON, Monkwell Street (Presbyterian). *Cups*: four, plain bowl with moulded rim, centre band, short stem with moulded base, two hollow handles. Inscription panel with decorative rectangular frame, (i) (Plate 12D) inscribed '*This Belongs to the | Society | of Protestant Dissenters in | Monks Well Street y^e Rev^d. | Mr Dan^ll Wilcox Pastor | 1729*'. London 1728, maker 'RB'. Weight '22=5'. (ii) as last, but London 1729. Weight '21=18'. (iii) inscribed as before except '*Samu^ll Lawrance MD: Pastor | 1735*'. London 1735, maker's mark on both handles, James Smith. Weight '22=5'. (iv) as last. Weight '22=12'. Sizes: (i–ii) H 6½, D 5¼, W 9¾; (iii–iv) H 6⅜, D 5⅜, W 9¾. [Society disbanded 1824; plate now at Dr Williams's Library]

(95) CITY OF LONDON, Old Jury (Presbyterian). *Cups*: (Plate 12C) four, plain bowl with moulded rim and base, two hollow handles. Inscribed '*For the use of the Protestant | Dissenting Church in ye old Jury | 1728*', and secondary inscription on underneath of two cups 'Dr. Williams's | Library'. London 1728, maker Gabriel Sleath. H 5⅛, D 5, W 8¾. *Plates*: four, numbered 1–4 and marked with the weight of each piece. Inscribed below '*The Gift of Saml Palmer late of Hackney Esqr to*

the Dissenting Congregation in the Old Jewry Anno 1733'. London 1720, maker Anthony Nelme. D 9⅝. [The cups were given to Dr Williams's Library before *c.* 1900; the plates which became the property of 'Unity Church', Islington [108], are now in the Museum of London]   [159]

(96) CITY OF LONDON, Silver Street, later Falcon Square, now Hindes Road, Harrow (Congregational/URC). [The following uninscribed and unmarked pewter vessels were deposited in 1916 in the Guildhall Museum, now the Museum of London: *Cups*: two. H 8. *Flagon*: H 11½, D base 6½. *Footed plates*: H 3½, D 7½, D base 3⅞. Probably early 19th-century or before]   [123]

(97) CITY OF LONDON. [The following unprovenanced items, now in Dr Williams's Library, probably come from former dissenting meetings in London. *Cups*: pair, plain bowl with everted rim, moulded base and two hollow handles. London 1723, maker Matthew Lofthouse. H 5¼, D 5, W 8½. *Plates*: two, base metal with central foot. H 2¾, D 10¼]

(98) BARNET, Golder's Green (Presbyterian). ['Four silver two-handled *cups* and two silver *plates* from the original communion plate of the old 18th-century Presbyterian foundation at Hackney were reported (*PHSJ*, IV (1931) 259) to have been added to the museum of the Presbyterian Historical Society, being part of a larger set of which 'two cups and four patens' were 'retained by the Congregation of St Ninian's, Golders Green, to whom the plate was lent by the Church and Committee of the Presbytery of London North on the foundation of the Congregation'. The items first mentioned were stolen *c.* 1945 from Presbyterian Church House and the cups were then believed to be two of 1836 and two of 1868, the congregation being possibly not Mare Street but one formed in 1863 in Dalston, moved to Hackney Downs in 1871, closed 1935. The items remaining at Finchley Road, Golders Green (Presbyterian/URC) are described below]

Cups: pair, plain bowl on stem with narrow band, moulded base, two double-curved handles, exceptionally light in weight. Sheffield 1818, maker's mark of John Fenton & Co. as reused by Fenton, Allanson & Co. of Norfolk Street. H 7, D 5⅛, W 9¼. *Plates*: four, probably Sheffield plate, minor variations in pattern, gadrooned band at edge. Two with maker's initials 'TW'. Early 19th-century. D 9¾.   [8]

(99) CAMDEN, Eagle Street, later 'Kingsgate Chapel', Catton Street (Baptist). [On the dissolution of the Church in 1961 the plate fell into the hands of the Baptist Union which sold the unique set of cups to a

purchaser in Canada; one cup previously on loan to Bristol Baptist College was subsequently donated to the College. *Cup*: (Frontis.) one of a set of twelve, inside gilt, bowl with everted rim, spherical knop and tall bell-shaped base. Engraved with a shield-of-arms *On a bend engrailed three roses, a label in sinister chief*; crest, *a bird bearing in its beak a key*. Inscribed on base '❋ The Gift of Bro^r Jno. Payne to the Protestant Dissenting Congregation in Eagle Street | – Baptized into a Personal Profession of Repentance towards God, & Faith in our Lord Jesus Christ. | October y^e 4th 1734' and marked inside base with vessel number and weight 'No.8 12=4½'. London 1734, maker's mark a crown above (illegible) initials. H 7¼, D 4⅝. *Flagon*: (Plate 23C) bulbous body, neck, lid with finial, handle with plaited wicker covering. Engraved with shield-of-arms *Three lozenges conjoined in fesse ermine*, for Gifford, impaling *on a bend sinister four roundels or, in chief a lion rampant, in base a dog passant*, for ?Paynter, motto 'MELIORA SPERO'. Inscribed 'THE GIFT OF ANDREW & GRACE GIFFORD TO THE PROTESTANT DISSENTING CONGREGATION OF BAPTISTS IN EAGLE STREET LONDON MDCCLX [*sic*]'. London, 1765, maker Francis Crump. H 15¼.   [30]

(100) CAMDEN, Kentish Town, Kelly Street (Congregational). *Cups*: pair, bowl with moulded everted rim, short stem and moulded base, two hollow handles. Inscribed below base *'the Meeting House at Stoke Newington Mar: 30 1739'*. London, 1738, maker ?'I.B'. H 4⅝, D 4, W 7½.

(101) CAMDEN, Rosslyn Hill (Presbyterian/Unitarian). *Cups*: four: (i) bowl, inside gilt, with slight upstand at base, two barbed handles, upper band of cable moulding and gadrooned lower third, oval cartouche with leaf-scroll surround. Inscribed below *'Sacram^t Cup | Hampstead Meeting | Nov.20.1731'*. London 1702, maker probably Samuel Dell. H 3¾, D 4¼, W 7¼. (ii) (Plate 16B) bowl, inside gilt, with slight upstand at base, two strap handles with moulded outer faces, upper cable moulding and gadrooned lower third, cartouche with naturalistic floral ornament. London 1764, maker William Cripps. H 3½, D 3¾, W 6½. (iii–iv) reproductions of early 18th-century style gadrooned two-handled cups but with excess of enrichment and cartouche on two sides, inside gilt. Inscribed below 'This cup and one like it | were presented by | Members of the Congregation | Feb.1.1895'. London (Britannia) 1894, maker 'JCB' for Carrington. H 3½, D 4, W 6⅝. *Flagon*: (Plate 23D) urn-shaped body on swept base, narrow neck, no lid, handle with insulated joints. London 1782, maker John Scofield. H 12¼.

Plates: two (i) with central foot and moulded base, engraved with shield-of-arms, quarterly, in a cartouche, arms worn or defaced. Inscribed below 'Mrs. Blunden's Gift to Hamps^d Meeting. Nov.20.1731.'. London 1709, maker Richard Green. H 2¾, D 8⅜. (ii) with central foot, inscribed below '*Rosslyn Hill Chapel, Hampstead | E.E. 1892 H.E. | Presented by Harriet, | Widow of Edward Enfield*'. London 1892, maker W. J. Barnard. H 2⅜, D 8½. [39]

(102) CAMDEN, West Street Chapel (Huguenot/Methodist). The following items were used by the Methodist congregation at West Street, the cups being transferred from the previous occupants, and subsequently at Great Queen Street and Kingsway Hall. *Cups*: two, plain bowl with moulded rim, baluster stem and moulded base. Inscribed 'HI DUO CALICES DONO DATI SUNT AB HONESTO VIRO PETRO FENOWILLET DIE OCTAVO JULII MDCIIIC IN USUM CONGREGATIONIS GALLICAE QUAE HABETUR IN VIA VULGO DICTA WEST STREET DE PAROECIA S. ÆGIDII; SI VERO DISSOLVITUR CONGREGATIO IN USUM PAUPERUM VENUND-ABUNTUR' (spelling 'FENOWILET' on one cup). Silver, but not marked, *c*.1697. H 7¾, D 3⅞. *Flagon*: pewter, tapered body, wide base, domed lid. Early 19th-century. H 11. [See also: *WHSP*, XVI (1927–8) 137; XXVII (1949–50) 104–5, 188. R.C.H.M. *West London* (1925) Holborn (3). Now in Wesley's House, City Road] [45]

(103) GREENWICH, Woolwich New Road, (Presbyterian/URC). *Cups*: three (i) plain bowl, stem and moulded base, gadrooned band. Inscribed below rim '*Scotch Church Woolwich 1801*'. London 1800, makers Richard Lockwood and John Douglas. H 5¾, D 3¾. (A second identical cup is also reported) (ii–iii) mugs, Sheffield plate, moulded band and base, hollow handle. Early 19th-century. H 5⅞, D 3¾. [77]

(104) HACKNEY, Mare Street, later St Thomas's Square (Presbyterian). *Cups*: pair, plain bowl on short stem with narrow band and moulded base, two double-curved handles. Inscribed '*Belonging to ye Congregation of Hackney Mr Billio Minister*', also, on underside, weight and date 'both: Cups | 25.12 | 1700'. London 1700, maker White Walsh. H 7, D 5, W 9¼. *Plates*: pair, cable moulding around edge. Inscribed at centre '1701' and around it 'Belonging to y^e Congregation of Hackney for ever — Mr Billio Minister ✳', and mark of weight below 'both 18oz = Less: 5dwtt'. London 1701, maker 'WI' in octagonal stamp for Edward Wimans. D 9¾. [Congregation dissolved 1896, plate now in Shoreditch District Library, Pitfield Street]

[Two two-handled cups and two plates, all silver, dated 1701, said to be from a Hackney congregation, possibly unrelated to the above, were reported stolen *c*.1945 from Presbyterian Church House] [84]

(105) HACKNEY, New Gravel Pit (Presbyterian/Unitarian). *Cups*: four, inside gilt, shaped bowl with stem, moulded base and two double-curved handles. London 1834, maker Charles Fox. H 6⅝, D 4⅜, W 7⅛. *Plates*: four. Date and maker as before. D 8¾. (The receipt for the above dated 6 June 1835 from James Bruce, jeweller, gold- and silversmith, No.5 Cranbourn Street, Leicester Square, describes the items as '4 Silver Pint Challices with two handles & Gilt inside 79oz 12dwt' and '4 Plain Silver Plates 48–14' together with 'A Wainscot Case, petitioned lined with baige & lock & key for the above', credit being given for '2 Silver Challices' 21oz 8dwt and '2 Silver Plates' 26oz 16dwt which those items replaced.) [Now at Essex Hall] [86]

(106) HACKNEY, Newington Green (Presbyterian/Unitarian). *Cups*: pair, plain bowl, moulded base, two handles. Inscribed '*The Congregation | at | Newington Green | 1733*'. London 1733, maker probably Gabriel Sleath. H 5, D 4½. *Plates*: pair, pewter, with crowned initials 'F over C M'. Touch of Richard Yates (C.5344), *c*.1800. D 9⅝. [90]

(107) HILLINGDON, Harlington (Baptist). *Plates*: pair, pewter, inscribed 'Harlington Chapel'. Touch of Samuel Ellis (C.1547), late 18th-century. D 9¾. [131]

(108) HILLINGDON, Old Meeting, Uxbridge (Presbyterian/Congregational/URC). *Cups*: pair, bowl with moulded rim, centre band, short stem with moulded base, two double-curved handles with leaf ornament. Inscribed '*Given by M^rs: Lethieullier to the | Presbyterian Church at Uxbridge | 1738*'. London 1738, maker Thomas Whipham. H 5⅜, D 4¾, W 8⅛. *Plate*: with central boss. Rim inscribed '*The Gift of M^rs: Halsey to the Presbyterian Church in Uxbridge Feb^ry: 1740*'. London 1740, maker John Swift. D 11¼. [132]

(109) HILLINGDON, Providence Chapel (Congregational). *Cup*: (Plate 4E) beaker with everted rim and moulded base. Inscribed within circle '*The Gift of | the Reverend | Nathan Webb | to The Church of Christ | in | Uxbridge | 1772*' and secondary inscription on reverse '*Gift to | Providence Congregational Church | Uxbridge England | from | First Congregational Church | Uxbridge Massachusetts | U.S.A. | September 22, 1930*'. Scratchings on base include '11-3' and '$12,98'. Colonial silver without assay or maker's mark. H 5¾, D 4. *Flagon*: base metal, spreading base, lid with finial. Mark, a pair of scales, early 19th-century. H 11¼.

[These items were transferred to the Old Meeting when the congregations united, 1962] [133]

(110) ISLINGTON, 'Unity Church', Upper Street, Islington (Presbyterian/Unitarian); formerly Little Carter Lane, City of London. *Cups*: (Plate 12E) four, plain bowl with slightly everted rim, moulded base, two handles. Inscribed beneath '*This belongs to the Congregation, in Carter lane May 1766:*'. London 1766, makers Thomas Whipman & Charles Wright. H 5¾, D 5, W 8⅞. Capacity one quart. *Flagons*: four, pewter, tapered body with moulded rim, upper band and spreading base, lid with finial, double-curved handle. Late 18th-century. H 11½. *Plates*: eight (i–iv) four. Inscribed 'The Gift of Saml Palmer late of Hackney Esqr to the Dissenting Congregation in the Old Jewry Anno 1733'. London 1720, maker ?Anthony Nelme. D 9⅝. (v–viii) four, pewter, with cinquefoiled edge. Touch of Joseph Spackman (C.4440), *c.*1760. D 9⅝. [All the above items are now in the Museum of London] [159]

(111) ISLINGTON, Hare Court, City of London, now St Pauls Road, Canonbury (Congregational/URC). [The following items, recorded and illustrated by J. B. Marsh (*The Story of Harecourt* (1871) 158–60) are no longer in the possession of the Church; they were reputed to date from the 17th century. *Cups*: (Plate 3A) four beakers, one plain, the others engraved with shields-of-arms of Sir Robert Tichbourne, ?Miss Champneys, and ?Thomas Fletcher. *Plates*: four, with broad rims engraved with shields-of-arms of Sir Bulstrode Whitelocke impaling those of Mary Wilson, his third wife. Hall-marks (not quoted) said to be identical with the plain cup. Also a later plate with lozenge-of-arms on rim] [147]

(112) KENSINGTON AND CHELSEA, Hornton Street, Kensington, later Allen Street (Congregational/URC). [Two *cups* are illustrated by C. Silvester Horne (*A Century of Christian Service* (1893), 36–7): one of lustreware, bowl with narrow band, stem and base, two handles, early 19th-century; second, base metal without handles] [168]

(113) LAMBETH, Stockwell Green (Congregational/URC). *Plates*: four, Sheffield plate. (i–iii) Inscribed 'Stockwell new Chapel | 1836'. D 9. (iv) similar inscription but without date. Early 19th-century. D 9¼. *Gallery tray*: Sheffield plate, on three ball feet. Inscribed as above but without date. Early 19th-century. H 2½, D 8¾. [190]

(114) LEWISHAM, High Street, Deptford (Congregational). *Cups*: six (i-ii) bowl with everted rim, slight upstand at base, two barbed handles, upper cable moulding and gadrooning to lower third, oval cartouche with crude scale surround and shell below. Inscribed on (i) '*The Gift | of E : Swallow | to the Church | in But=lane | Deptford. | 1708*'; on (ii) the same, but '*A : Swallow*'. London 1707, maker Jonathan Madden. H 4½, D 4¾, W 7½. (iii–iv) (Plate 9C) tall slightly tapered bowl with everted rim, hollow stem with moulded band and moulded base. Inscribed '*The Gift of Mrs Anne Ligoe : *'. London 1715, maker Matthew Lofthouse. H 9½, D 4⅝. (v–vi) tulip-shaped bowl, inside gilt, on narrow hollow stem with prominent band and moulded base. Inscribed on (v) '*Congregational Church, | High Street, Deptford, | Presented by the | Misses Elizabeth & Maria Hopkins, | May, 1878.*'; on (vi) the same but '*Mr. Joseph Gideon Slous*'. London assay (v) 1870; (vi) 1874; maker 'SS', possibly Stephen Smith. H 8¾, D 3⅝. *Flagon*: (Plate 24B) cylindrical body with thin moulded middle and lower bands, spreading base, domed lid with gadrooned edge. Engraved below spout with 'IHS' in sunburst, inscribed on base 'Presented by the Members of the Church | High Street Chapel Deptford June 1845. | Mrs ISABELLA MORISON AND OTHERS'. London 1845, makers R. Pearce & G. Burrows. H 11¼. *Plates*: eight (i–ii) with gadrooned edge. Inscribed on (i) '*The Gift : of Mr Timothy Robinson deceased and Mary his wife to Mr Beaumonts Congregation Meeting in Butt': Lane Deptford TO:TF 1707/8*'; on (ii) the same except 'Dec^{d} : &' and 'Meeting'. London (i) 1703, maker ?DM; (ii) 1707, maker William Gamble. D 9. (iii–iv) similar pattern to last. Inscribed 'Presented by the Members of the Church | High Street Chapel Deptford, October 1859'. London 1859, maker 'WS', probably William Smiley. D 9¼. (v–vii) similar pattern to last. Inscribed on (v) 'Presented by Mrs A. E. Lockyer to the Congregational Church, High St., Deptford. | In memory of her beloved husband, George Lockyer, deacon, died August 15. 1880'; on (vi) 'Presented by the Rev^{d} S-Sabine Read to the Congregational Church, High St., Deptford. | In memory of his beloved wife, Emma Margaret, died, 30th October, 1883.'; on (vii) 'Presented by Richard Trickett to the Congregational Church, High St., Deptford, | In memory of his beloved wife Ann, died, 16th June 1884'. London 1884, maker 'S over J H in shield'. (vii) is also marked 'GOLDSMITHS ALLIANCE | LIMITED | CORNHILL LONDON'. D 9¼. (viii) Sheffield plate. Inscribed below '*High Street Chapel | Deptford | 1857*'. Makers' initials 'JM & B'. [now in the V&A] [197]

(115) SOUTHWARK, Deadmans Place, later Union Street, latterly 'Church of the Pilgrim Fathers', New Kent Road (Congregational/URC). *Cups*: (Plate 2B)

four beakers with slightly everted rim and moulded base, band of leaf scroll ornament below rim including date '1691'. The original set is reputed to have been given to the church in or about 1694 (?1691) by the minister, the Rev. Jonathan Owen 'a man of considerable wealth' (see Cleal (1908) 10, and *CHST* III (1907–8) 153–4). Three of the cups are now late 18th-century replicas but these appear to reproduce the differences in detail on the decorative bands of their predecessors whose worn condition, to judge by that of the survivor, necessitated their replacement. London: (i) 1691, maker 'GM between mullets'; (ii) 1766, maker's mark worn, '?Priest'; (iii) 1769, maker 'IK'; (iv) 1772, maker 'IK'. H 5¼, D 4. Capacity about one quart. [now in the V&A] *Plates*: four, with narrow reeded edge and central boss. (i–ii) Inscribed below rim 'A-Present-from-Geo*e*-Evans-Esquire-to-the-Society-of-Protestant-Dissenters-which-removed-from-Deadmans-Place-to-Union-Street-Southwark-in-1788', and on one a feint incomplete or partly erased inscription on the central boss '*A Present from Geo-Evans Esq*ʳ *Sen*ʳ *to the Society of Protestant Dissenters Assembling ... '*. London 1788, maker 'EF', possibly Edward Fernell. D 10½. (iii–iv) inscribed below rim '*A.D.1825 The property of a Society of Protestant Dissenters meeting in Union Street Southwark, (formerly of Deadman's Place)'*. London 1824, maker 'WS'. D 10⅜. [Also referred to in *CHST* (*loc. cit.* above) are four pewter *plates*, a *flagon*, two candlesticks and snuffers: no longer in possession of the church] [224]

(116) WALTHAM FOREST, New Meeting, Marsh Street, now 'Trinity', Walthamstow (Congregational/URC). *Cup*: plain bowl, stem with gadrooned knop, enriched base. Inscribed underneath '*The Gift of W*ᵐ *Parker Esq*ʳ *for the use of Walthamstow new Meeting House 1787*'. London 1787, maker John Denziloe. H 7⅞, D 4. (An identical cup is also reported) *Plates*: two. Inscription, date and maker as above. D 9⅝. [243]

(117) WANDSWORTH (Methodist). [*Cup*: Britannia metal, plated, plain bowl on stem with knop. Inscribed below rim 'A GIFT TO THE REV. MR JOHN WESLEY FOR THE USE OF THE WANDSWORTH SOCIETY'. Probably late 18th-century. H 8½, D 4. Reported in *WHSP* XXVII (1949–50) 105, as being in the museum, Wesley's Chapel, City Road.]

(118) WESTMINSTER, King's Weigh House (Congregational). *Cups*: nine (i–vi) six, slightly tapered bowl with everted rim, hollow stem and moulded base. (i) London 1696, maker 'I intersecting S' for John Sutton, scratched weight '21=8'; (ii) (Plate 9A) As last, but weight '21=6'; (iii) Inscribed around lower edge of base '*The gift of Robert Trad*'. London 1697, maker 'SV' for John Sutton; (iv) London 1702, maker Joseph Ward, weight '21=0'; (v) London 1699, maker William Andrews; (vi) London 1705, maker Joseph Ward. H 8¾, D 5. Also several later cups: (vii) light metal bowl, gilt inside, set in elaborately enriched mount having tall stem, knop with three cherubs' heads, and base with repoussé decoration. Maker 'FTA', late 19th-century. H 8½, D 3¼, D base 4¾. (viii–ix) pair, hammered surface, tapered bowl with enriched lower half, on tall stem and base. London 1899, maker (signed) Gilbert Marks. H 8½, D 3½. *Flagon*: (Plate 24A) cylindrical body with lower band, moulded base, domed lid with finial, double-curved handle. Inscribed '*To the | REVEREND THOMAS BINNEY, | PASTOR, | And the Deacons and Members of the | CHURCH of CHRIST, | Assembling for Divine Worship at the | KING'S WEIGH HOUSE CHAPEL, FISH STREET HILL, | IN THE CITY OF LONDON. | This Flagon is presented as a grateful memorial | of their long continued kindness & confidence | by their brother and servant in Christ, | JOHN REMINGTON MILLS, | March 25th 1846.'*. London 1844, makers Edward, Edward jnr., John & William Barnard. H 14 overall. *Plate*: one, with six-foil border, on three short feet. London 1749, maker William Peaston. D 12¼. *Baptismal basin*: (Plate 27A) rounded hammered bowl with moulded and gadrooned base and gadrooned rim. Inscribed beneath '*This Belongs to the Meeting House in Eastcheap at the Weighouse*'. London 1697, maker Joseph Ward. H 3⅞, D 9⅛. [Congregation dissolved 1966; the above items are now in the Museum of London, excepting cups (v–vi) which are at Bala-Bangor College, Bangor, North Wales, details of which were kindly supplied by the Principal, the Revd Dr R. Tudur Jones] [261]

HAMPSHIRE

(119) ANDOVER, East Street (Congregational/URC). Plated base metal set of four *cups*, four *plates* and *flagon*, all inscribed with date 1844. *Flagon*: 'Presented by Henry Goddard'. Also two matching plates dated 1876. [6]

(120) EAST WOODHAY, former Highclere Chapel (Congregational). *Plates*: two, pewter. Touch of Samuel Smith, mid-18th-century. D 8¾. [Chapel (SU 437606) closed, plate now in private hands.]

(121) PORTSMOUTH, High Street (Presbyterian/Unitarian). *Cups*: (Plate 17A–D) four (i–iii) all with S-shaped sides to bowl, slight upstand at base and pair of cast double-curved handles with head finials. Lower half of bowl decorated with hunting scenes in repoussé. (i) With figures of hunting dog and unicorn. Base

inscribed 'E over D M' and weight '6oz 0gr'. London 1659, maker's mark 'RH, a cinquefoil and two pellets below'. H 3¼ to rim 3¾ overall, D 4, W 6⅝. (ii) With figures of hunting dog and stag. Inscribed below rim 'A∗H' and on underside '*The Gift of Mrs Ann Howel – 1718 | to this Church, w^tt 6^z–13^dw–0^gr*', also scratched weight '6–14–6'. London 1668, maker's mark 'TK, cinquefoil below'. H 3, D 3¾, W 6¼. (iii) With figures similar to last. Inscribed on underside '∗A∗L∗', pecked inscription '8oz 2dwt' and later scratching '7oz 17dw 6gr'. London 1669, maker not recorded. H 3, D 4, W 6¼. (iv) Bowl with everted rim, straight sides rounded to short upstand at base, lower third gadrooned, cable moulding between two S-shaped handles. Inscribed on underside 'C over P F' and scratched weight and date '6oz 8dw 6gr | 1698'. London 1698, maker's mark 'RO' for ?Alexander Roode. H 3½, D 4⅜, W 6¾.

[The above are now at the City Museum, Portsmouth. Evans (1897) 201–4, also records a base metal set of *flagon* and four *plates* inscribed with the date 1849. Unlocated] [49]

(122) RINGWOOD (Presbyterian/Unitarian). [Evans (1897) 209–10, records a small uninscribed silver *cup* with floral decoration, weight 5oz 14dwt, date uncertain, bequeathed 1871 but probably earlier. H 3¾, D 4. Unlocated] [50]

(123) NEWPORT, Isle of Wight (General Baptist/ Unitarian). *Cup*: one mug, slightly tapered barrel-shaped body, moulded rim and base, vertical gadrooning to lower third and upper cable moulding. Single hollow handle, opposite which is a small and crudely scrolled cartouche enclosing the initials 'C over I I' for John and Jane Cooke, and a later inscription alongside '*Unitarian Chapel*'. Exeter 1724, maker 'PE with pellet above, in oval', for Philip Elston. H 3⅝, D 2¾ at rim, 3⅛ at base, W 4⅜. Communion set comprising *Cup*: standing cup, interior gilt, with moulded everted rim, octofoil decoration in lower half, on stem with moulded knop and octofoil base. Bowl inscribed 'PRESENTED BY | William Mortimer | 24th August 1862'. London 1862, maker's mark 'JS' or 'TS' in double circle. H 8¼, D 3⅞. *Flagon*: octofoil body and base, lid with finial, spout, handle. Inscription and maker as last. H 11½. *Plates*: two (i) cinquefoil rim, on central foot. Inscription and maker as before. H 2¾, D 9¼. (ii) as last but with longer inscription 'PLATE FOR THE COMMUNION SERVICE CONSISTING OF FLAGON, CHALICE, PATEN & PLATE | presented to the | Trustees of the Unitarian Chapel | Newport, Isle of Wight, | Re^D Tho^S F. Thomas, Minister, | August 24th, 1862, by | William Mortimer, | Senior member and

Trustee | as a Bi-Centenary Memorial of the | Two Thousand Ejected Clergymen'. [86]

HEREFORDSHIRE

(124) ROSS URBAN, Gloucester Road, Ross on Wye (Congregational/URC). *Cups*: (Plate 9B) pair, slightly tapered bowl with everted rim, on wide hollow stem and moulded base. Uninscribed. London (Britannia) 1706, Maker Humphrey Payne. H 7⅛, D 4, at base 3¾. *Flagon*: Sheffield plate, shaped body, domed lid, spout, handle with heart-shaped lower terminal, on narrow stem and base. Inscribed 'INDEPENDENT | CHAPEL | ROSS | 1839'. H 11. [40]

HERTFORDSHIRE

(125) BRAUGHING, Fleece Lane (Congregational). *Plate*: pewter, rim engraved with crest of a boar's head gorged with a coronet issuing from a mural crown. Touch of John Hulls of London (C.2452), *c*.1800. D 9⅝. [16]

(126) CHIPPERFIELD (Baptist). Communion set, pewter, comprising two cups, flagon and two plates. Each inscribed '*The Gift | of | Richard Davis | to the Communicants of the Dissenting Meeting | at Chipperfield, | Herts | 1st August 1821*' (Last line erased). *Cups*: pair, plain straight-sided bowl on hollow stem with moulded band and moulded base. Unmarked. H 8¾, D 3½. *Flagon*: plain body on moulded base with spout, double-curved handle and domed lid with finial. Inscription below spout. H 11¾, D of base 6½. *Plates*: pair. Inscription around rim. Touch 'COMPTON' in oval, for Townsend Compton (C.1065). D 9¾.

[Plate dispersed but recovered for church *c*.1960 by public subscription] [20]

(127) HEMEL HEMPSTEAD, Box Lane (Congregational). *Plates*: pewter, pair, with upturned rim and initials '?W over M S'. Touch of Benjamin Blackwell (C.437a), mid-18th-century. D 9½. [31]

(128) HEMEL HEMPSTEAD, Marlowes (Baptist). *Plates*: seven, pewter (i) initials ' C over TE' on rim. Touch of Stephen Bridges (C.572), *c*.1700. D 9¼. (ii–iii) pair. Touch of Thomas Compton (C.1063), early 19th-century. D 11. (iv–v) pair. Touch of Samuel Cocks (C.1004), early 19th-century. D 9½. (vi–vii) pair. Marks include shield with bend between four ?thistles, maker not traced. D 9¼. [33]

(129) HEMEL HEMPSTEAD, Salem Chapel, Two Waters (Strict Baptist). *Plates*: six, pewter. Touch of Thomas Compton (C.1004), early 19th-century. D 9⅝. [34]

HUNTINGDON AND PETERBOROUGH

(130) GREAT GIDDING (Baptist). *Cup*: Sheffield plate, bowl with everted rim, two reeded strap handles, moulded base closed with wooden insert. Late 18th-century. H 5¼, D 3¾, W 6¼.   [13]

KENT

(131) CANTERBURY, Blackfriars (General Baptist/ Unitarian). *Cups*: four, Sheffield plate, inside gilt, plain rounded bowl on stem and base. *c*.1800. H 6⅜, D 3⅝. *Flagon*: electroplate, with elaborately decorated handle and finial of lily. Late 19th-century, probably domestic. H 10½. *Plates*: plated base metal, reeded edge. Mid-19th-century. D 9¼.   [23]

(132) CHEVENING, Bessels Green (General Baptist/ Unitarian). *Cups*: pair, pewter, hemispherical bowl on moulded stem and base. Unmarked, 18th century. H 6¼, D 4¾. *Plates*: pair, pewter. Initials 'S over D M' on base. Touch of Richard Norfolk (C.3409), mid-18th-century. D 14¾.   [28]

(133) CRANBROOK, Providence Chapel (Calvinistic Independent/Strict Baptist). Electroplate set by Dixon & Sons, brought from Galeed Chapel, Brighton *c*.1909 when Strict Baptist church formed. Comprises pair of thistle-shaped *cups*, *flagon* and four *plates*.   [34]

(134) DEAL, High Street (General Baptist/Unitarian). Electroplate set by 'E.M. & Co', *c*.1857, comprising *Cups*: two, plain bowl on swept stem and base. H 8¼, D 3¾. *Flagon*: spout, handle, domed lid, side engraved with 'IHS' in sunburst. H 11¾. *Plate*: with enriched border, centre engraved with 'IHS'. Base with 'This Plate with the Flagon and Cups was presented by MR. RICHARD CHAMBERLAIN to the Unitarian Congregation of Deal during the ministry of the Revd. Iden Payne January 1857'. Numbered on base '1567'. D 10½.   [38]

(135) DOVER, Adrian Street (General Baptist/Unitarian). Electroplate set, given 1844, comprising *Cups*: pair, interior gilt, plain bowl with everted rim, stem with knop, moulded base. Unmarked. H 6¼, D 3⅜. *Flagon*: (Plate 24D) tall straight-sided body with lid, spout, handle with heart-shaped lower terminal and moulded base. Inscribed below spout: '*This* | COMMUNION SERVICE | *was presented by some friends of* | RELIGIOUS LIBERTY | *to the* | **General Baptist Church** | *assembling for worship in* | ADRIAN STREET CHAPEL | **Dover** | *in commemoration of the passing of the* | DISSENTERS' CHAPELS BILL. | 1844.'. Maker's mark 'E & Co crowned in shield' for Elkington. H 11½. *Plates*: three, marked 'E & Co'. D 9⅛.   [42]

(136) MAIDSTONE, Earl Street (Presbyterian/Unitarian). [Evans (1897) 162–4, lists the following: *Cups*: (i) 'Porringer-shape'. London 1692. H 3. (ii) inscribed 'The Gift of Mrs Cath. Harris, for the use of the Meeting, 1774'. H 5½. (He also gives this as London 1653–4, but probably mistakenly for 1771, see Jones (1905–6) 285) Also electroplate *Flagon* and two *Plates*. All items sold 1919].   [88]

(137) SANDWICH (Congregational/URC). *Cup*: bowl, inside gilt, with everted rim, short hollow stem on moulded base, two hollow handles. Inscribed '*Belonging to the Congregation* | *of Protestant Dissenters* | *at Sandwich in Kent 1758*'. London 1757, makers Richard Gurney & Thomas Cooke. H 5⅞, D 4, W 7⅛. *Cup*: electroplate copy of last. Inscribed 'Sandwich | Congregational Church | 1882'. H 5⅞, D 4, W 7⅛. *Flagon*: electroplate. Inscribed as last. H 12¾. *Plates*: pair. Inscribed in base 'Donum Elgar'. London 1708, maker John Read. D 8½.   [117]

(138) TENTERDEN, Old Meeting, Ashford Road (Presbyterian/Unitarian). *Cups*: (Plate 18B–D) four (i) bowl with S-shaped sides, everted rim, slight upstand at base, and two cast handles with head finials. Repoussé decoration to lower half of large flowers and leaves. London 1661, maker's mark 'GD with cinquefoil below in heart-shaped punch'. H 3⅜, D 3⅞, W 6⅝. (ii) similar to last, but decoration includes a hunting dog and a stag. Inscription below rim in pricked cartouche 'T over A A' possibly for Andrew and Ann Tucker. London 1668, maker's mark 'IW in shield'. H 3½, D 4⅛, W 6½. (iii–iv) beakers, pair, Sheffield plate, inside gilt, plain. Unmarked, *c*.1800, said to be the gift of Robert Milligan Shipman. H 14¼ [Cups sold 1974]   [140]

LANCASHIRE

(139) ASHTON-IN-MAKERFIELD, Park Lane (Presbyterian/Unitarian). *Cups*: four (i–ii) base metal, plain bowl on swept stem and base. Mark of Richard Constantine, *c*.1800. H 6⅞, D 3⅞. (iii–iv) base metal, plain bowl on stem with knop. Inscribed 'PRESENTED | to Park Lane Chapell by | Mrs Esther Broadbent'. Mid-19th-century. H 8¼, D 4⅜. *Plates*: two (i) pewter, with crowned rose and 'London' label. D 9¼. (ii) base metal. Inscribed as on cups iii and iv. Maker 'B & A S' for Broadhead & Atkin, Sheffield, mid-19th-century. D 10¼. *Flagon*: base metal. Inscribed 'Presented by Ann Elizabeth and Margaret Shaw 1858'. H 10½.   [4]

(140) ATHERTON, Chowbent (Presbyterian/Unitarian). *Cups*: two (i) (Plate 7A) tapered bowl on baluster stem and spreading base. Bowl inscribed '.R✳M.' for Robert Mort of Wharton Hall. London 1652, maker's mark 'a bird or martlet in shield'. H 6¾, D rim

3¾, base 3⅝. (ii) similar design and inscription to last but larger. London 1653, maker's mark 'M in heart-shaped indent'. H 7¼, D rim 4⅛ base 3⅞. *Flagon*: Sheffield plate, tapered body with lower band, moulded base, domed lid with tall thumb rest, S-shaped handle with heart-shaped lower terminal, spout. Early 19th-century. H 9⅝. *Plate*: pewter, raised on central hollow stem and wide base, London label and 'hard metal', possibly by Henry Bell or Bells (C.369). H 3⅜, D 9⅛.
[12]

(141) AUDENSHAW, Red Hall Chapel (Methodist New Connexion). *Cups*: pair, base metal, tapered bowl on tall stem and spreading base. Lightly engraved decoration but uninscribed. c. 1795. H 8⅝, D 4½. *Plate*: of similar metal, date and decoration as cups, supported by three short legs. D 7, H 1.
[13]

(142) BLACKBURN, Chapel Street (Congregational). A Sheffield plate set, c. 1840 [now at Tockholes (168) below] similar in design to one from Great George Street, Liverpool (see (149) below), comprises *Cup*: H 8½, D 3½. *Flagon*: H 15¾. *Plates*: four, D 9¼. [237]

(143) BOLTON, Bridge Street (Wesleyan Methodist). *Cup*: (Plate 28A) rounded bowl on stem and square base. Inscriptions, on bowl 'Bridge Street Chapel', below base 'By Thos Moss 1803' (probably the donor). Sheffield 1802 by Thomas Lamborn. H 6¼, D 3⅝. (A second, similar, cup is reported to be in private possession). *Flagon*: Sheffield plate, body with two narrow reeded bands. Inscribed below base 'Bridge Street Chapel by Thos Moss 1803'. H 12⅛.
[27]

(144) CHORLEY, Chorley Chapel (Presbyterian/Unitarian). *Cups*: two (i) plain bowl, slightly everted rim, rounded above moulded base, two barbed S-shaped handles. Bowl inscribed '*The* GIFT OF M^R AB^M CROMPTON *To CHORLEY CHAPEL*'. London 1702, maker 'Lo in shield'. H 4½, D 4⅛, W 6⅞. (ii) plain bowl, everted rim, plain base and with two strap handles moulded on outer face. Inscribed as before. Chester 1747, maker Richard Richardson. H 3½, D 4, W 6¾.
[54]

(145) COLTON, Tottlebank (Baptist). *Cup*: base metal, plain bowl on short stem and hollow base, two handles. c. 1800. H 6½, D 4⅛, W 8¼. *Plate*: base metal with narrow gadrooned edge. D 8¾.
[64]

(146) CROFT, Risley Chapel (Presbyterian). Base metal set acquired in part on the transfer of the chapel from Unitarian trustees in 1839. *Cups*: two, bowl with moulded rim on stem with knop and base. H 8¼, D 4½. *Flagon*: slightly tapered body with central band, moulded base, domed lid, spout and hollow handle. H 12. *Plates*: three (i) Inscribed 'RISLEY PRESBYTERIAN

CHURCH FOUNDED 1662: CHURCH BUILT 1706 PURCHASED BY THE PRESBYTERY OF LANCASHIRE OCTOBER 30TH 1843 Rev. ALEXANDR RENNISON MA., ORDAINED FEBRUARY 6TH 1839.'. D 4. (ii) plain. Mid-19th-century. D 12¼. (iii) with decorated border. Late 19th-century. D 12½. [66]

(147) LANCASTER, St Nicholas Street (Presbyterian/Unitarian). *Cup*: bowl with everted rim, moulded base and two hollow handles, upper band of cable moulding between handles, lower half gadrooned. Plain circular cartouche in scrolled surround on one face. London 1715, maker William Fleming; handles separately stamped by Francis Garthorne. H 4⅞, D 4¼, W 7⅛. *Plate*: electroplate, on central hollow stem. Inscribed on upper face with 'IHS' in sunburst and 'PRESENTED TO THE CONGREGATION OF ST NICHOLAS STREET CHAPEL LANCASTER BY M^RS HUTCHINSON OF LUNE VILLA OCT^R 4TH 1862'. Maker James Dixon & Sons, Sheffield. [106]

(148) LIVERPOOL, Ancient Chapel of Toxteth (Presbyterian/Unitarian). *Cup*: plated base metal, plain bowl on tall stem with knop and spreading base. Inscribed 'Presented to the Reverend High Anderson & Members of the Park Chapel by their Friend Iohn Richardson'. Early 19th-century. [Evans (1897) 140–1, also refers to several other items with this inscription, said to replace a set stolen from the chapel] [118]

(149) LIVERPOOL, Great George Street (Congregational). *Cups*: eight (i–vi) (Plate 29D) Sheffield plate, inside gilt, tapered bowl with everted rim, petaloid decoration to lower half, on stem with knop and foliated base. Inscription on face 'Presented to the Church | *under the Pastoral care of* | The Rev: T. Raffles L.L.D. | *By the Ladies of the* | *Church and Congregation* | LIVERPOOL, MDCCCXL'. Maker's stamp, 'hand in rectangular sinking'. H 9⅛–9¼, D 4½. (vii–viii) electroplate, similar to last but knop slightly lower. Similarly inscribed but probably of later date. Maker 'H W & Co' and on base panel 'Wordley & Co, Lord Street, Liverpool'. *Flagons*: pair, Sheffield plate, tall petaloid body, moulded base, rim, spout with ornament below, hollow handle, lid with foliage finial. Inscription and stamp as on cups i–vi. Maker's initials 'J⁕P'. H 17¼. *Plates*: eight (i–vi) six, Sheffield plate, foliated rim. Inscribed and stamped as for cups i–vi. (vii–viii) two, electroplate. Similarly inscribed and same maker as cups vii-viii. D 4¾.
[123]

(150) LIVERPOOL, Renshaw Street, later Ullet Road (Presbyterian/Unitarian). *Cups*: pair, bowl with everted rim and double curved lower section above tall stem with moulded band and base. Inscribed below base

'1755'. London 1754, makers Richard Gurney & Thomas Cooke. H 10⅛, D 4⅝. *Plates*: pair. Inscribed above with 'IHS' in sunburst and below 'These Plates are presented to *Renshaw Street Chapel* BY THE JUNIOR MEMBERS of the Congregation during the Ministry of THE REVEREND I. H. THOM Anno Domini 1851'. London 1849, makers Edward, John and William Barnard. D 9. [130]

(151) LIVERPOOL, Kay Street, later Hope Street (Presbyterian/Unitarian). *Cups*: pair, bowl with everted rim and short moulded base, moulded band between two double-curved handles. Bowl inscribed 'THE GIFT OF *Mrs M. Clough to Kay Street Meeting House LIVERPOOL 1762*'. London 1761, maker Francis Crump. H 6⅝, D 4⅝. *Plates*: pair, rim enriched with six quatrefoiled roundels. Inscribed below 'E. FLOWER – SILVERSMITH – LIVERPOOL'. Birmingham 1849, maker 'E & Co'. [131]

(152) LIVERPOOL, Gateacre Chapel (Presbyterian/Unitarian). *Cup*: (Plate 14D) bowl with gadrooned lower part, short enriched base and two handles. Oval cartouche on front face inscribed '*The Cup of Blessing given to the Church at Gate-Acre by Joseph Lawton and bought in part by Isabel Heys her Legacy to him A.D. 1746*', also on underside '1714'. London 1703, maker Alice Sheene. H 5, D 5¾. *Plate*: plain. London 1766, makers Thomas Whipham & Charles Wright. D 9. *Baptismal basin*: plated base metal. Inscribed 'J. W.'. 19th-century. H 2¾, D 7¼. [131]

(153) LIVERPOOL, Domestic Mission, Mill Street (Unitarian). *Cups*: two (i) plain bowl on tall stem with knop. Sheffield 1922, maker 'W & H'. H 7¾, D 3¾. (ii) plated base metal on stem. Inscribed '*Presented to the Liverpool Domestic Mission by a Few Friends 1851*'. H 7⅝, D 3⅝. *Plates*: two, plated. Inscribed as last. D 9¼. [131]

(154) MANCHESTER, Cross Street (Presbyterian/Unitarian). *Cups*: five (i–iii) tapered bowl with moulded rim on hollow stem with moulded knop and base. Each engraved on face with crest of a stag's head issuing from a mural crown, owner's name below, '*N. Gaskell*' with 'Ex Dono' inserted above it. London 1718, maker Humphrey Payne. Sizes vary: H 9⅜, 9⅝, 10⅛, D 4¾–4⅞. (iv) similar to last. Uninscribed. London 1752, makers William Shaw & William Priest. H 9⅝, D 4¾. (v) plain bowl with everted rim, moulded base, two handles with heart-shaped lower terminals. Inscribed '*The Gift of Anne Bayley – 1790 –*'. Sheffield 1790, makers Nathaniel Smith & Co. H 5⅝, D 4, W 7. *Flagons*: (Plate 23A) two (i) tall body on moulded base, domed lid, handle, no spout. Engraved and inscribed as cups i–iii. Same assay and maker. H 12. (ii) similar pattern as last but not engraved or inscribed. Assay and maker as cup iv. H 11½. *Plates*: three, plain with central hollow foot. Engraved and inscribed as on cups i–iii. Same assay and maker. H 2½, D 9. [136]

(155) MANCHESTER, Gorton (Presbyterian/Unitarian). *Cups*: pair, bowl with gadrooned lower part and upper cable moulding between two barbed handles, slight upstand at base, plain oval cartouche on front face. London 1720, maker Thomas Folkingham. H 3½, D 4⅛, W 6½. *Plates*: pair, pewter, with plain broad rim. Touch of Samuel Smith of London (C.4279), after 1728. D 9¾. [145]

(156) MANCHESTER, Platt Chapel (Presbyterian/Unitarian). *Cups*: two (i) (Plate 1A) shallow bowl with two small barbed handles, sides engraved with formal floral ornament and a blind oval cartouche at the front. London 1641, maker Thomas Maundy. H to rim 2¼, D 4¼, W 6⅜. (ii) (Plate 18A) S-shaped bowl with two handles having double-headed finials. Lower part with floral repoussé decoration and oval cartouche at front inscribed 'A : I :'. London 1660, maker's mark in oval frame 'W G between mullets and pellets'. H to rim 3¾, D 4⅜, W 7. (The cups, sold in 1874, were repurchased for the congregation in 1895) [146]

(157) MANCHESTER, Lloyd Street (Presbyterian). *Cup*: (Plate 28B) plain bowl on hollow stem and square base. Added inscription 'Lloyd Street CHAPEL 1801 – 1858'. Newcastle 1803–20 (date letter missing), maker John Robertson. H 6¼, D 3⅝. *Dish*: Sheffield plate, oval on four short feet. Inscribed as above on underside. Maker Morton and Co., *c.* 1800. W 9¾ x 12¾. [Now in URCHS collection]

(158) MANCHESTER, Grosvenor Street (Congregational). *Cup*: Sheffield plate with circular silver insert for inscription, inside gilt, plain bowl with moulded silver rim, tall hollow stem and moulded base closed with circular disc. Inscribed 'GROSVENOR STREET *Chapel* MANCHESTER *Opened* DEC^R 3^D 1807'. *Flagon*: Sheffield plate, slightly tapered body with moulded centre band, moulded base, domed lid with thumb rest, spout and hollow handle. Inscribed on silver insert below spout, as on cup, also secondary inscription at side '*Presented to* MR JOHN L HULME on his 74th Birthday by the members of Roby Congregational Church AS A TOKEN OF AFFECTIONATE APPRECIATION OF 25 YEARS SERVICE AS A DEACON'. H 10⅞. (The church was renamed 'Roby' on removal *c.* 1912 to Dickenson Road, Rusholme)

(159) MANCHESTER, Zion Chapel, Hulme (Congregational). *Cups*: four (i–iii) Sheffield plate, inside

gilt, tall petaloid bowl on stem with moulded knop and base. Inscribed below base 'ZION *Independent Chapel HULME* Manchester'. Maker 'J. O', mid-19th-century. H 8½, D 3¾. (iv) generally similar to last but more strongly shaped. Similarly inscribed. *Flagons*: two, Sheffield plate, with tall petaloid body, base, lid with foliage finial, hollow handle and spout with decoration. Contemporary with cups and similarly inscribed. H 16½. *Plates*: four, all inscribed as above. (i–ii) Sheffield plate, cinquefoiled border. Maker 'W. W'. D 10¼. (iii–iv) electroplate, with 6-foiled border. Maker Walker & Hall, Sheffield, early 20th-century. D 10.

(160) MANCHESTER, Congregational College, Whalley Range. *Cup*: coconut cup reputed to have belonged to Oliver Heywood, comprising half shell of a coconut supported on a hollow base with three silver vertical bands and rim. Inscriptions, on rim '*Oliver Heywood's 1629–1702*', under base 'L / I*M' and scratched date 1743. No assay marks visible, but maker's initials 'WS' on rim. H 5, D 3⅞.

(161) NETHER WYERSDALE, Scorton (Wesleyan Methodist). *Cups*: pair, with sharply tapered bowl on stem with splayed and reeded base, ornamental band below rim. Secondary inscription on face within octofoil cartouche '*Presented by G FISHWICK for the use of the WESLEYAN SOCIETY at Scorton Decr 1842*'. London 1796, maker 'HN' possibly Henry Nutting. H 5¾, D 3. [158]

(162) RADCLIFFE, Cockey Moor Chapel, Ainsworth (Presbyterian/Unitarian). *Cups*: pair, plain bowl with everted rim on short stem and moulded base, two double-curved handles with leaf ornament. Uninscribed. London 1775, maker 'I.K' for John King. H 5½, D 4¼, W 7. *Flagon*: glass with silver mountings. Late 19th-century. *Plate*: plated base metal. Late 19th-century. D 10. [188]

(163) RADCLIFFE, Stand Chapel (Presbyterian/Unitarian). *Cup*: (Plate 15B) bowl on short gadrooned base, everted rim, gadrooned lower half and cable moulded band between pair of handles. Circular cartouche on front surmounted by cherub's head and inscribed 'W / W*M' for William and Margaret Walker; large inscription at back 'The gift of Margaret Walker | to th' Stand Chapel 1759'. London 1705, maker ?'WI', probably John Wisdome. H 4¾, D 5⅛, W 7⅝. *Plates*: two (i) circular with decorative border and supported on three claw feet. Engraved with crest of a bird and inscribed 'The gift of Louisa Potter to the Stand Chapel 1893'. London 1819, makers Joseph Craddock & William Reid. D 10¼. (ii) pewter. Touch of 'I:Brown' (possibly John Brown(e) of Gloucester), pre-1720 (C.639). D 9¼. *Wine funnel or 'tundish'*: pewter. 18th-century. H 3⅝. [189]

(164) RAMSBOTTOM, Summerseat (Wesleyan Methodist). Sheffield plate set comprising pair of *cups* with shaped bowl on stem and flared foot. H 10. Also *flagon*, footed *plate* and plain *plate*. Mid-19th-century. [201]

(165) RAMSBOTTOM, St Andrews (Presbyterian, Anglican since 1871). (Plate 30) All items except the last are inscribed 'THIS PIECE OF PLATE, PRESENTED BY ISABELLA GRANT OF SPRINGSIDE TO ST ANDREWS CHURCH RAMSBOTTOM, 1834' and enriched with 'IHS' within sunburst. London 1833, maker William Ker Reid. *Cups*: pair, narrow tapered bowl on stem and base. H 8⅜, D 3¾. *Flagon*: body with plain straight sides and moulded lower band on moulded base, domed lid with thumb rest, handle with leaf ornament, spout. H 12, D base 7½. *Alms-dish*: circular with enriched rim 'glory edge'. D 16. *Baptismal basin*: plain bowl with narrow moulded rim and plain upstand at base. H 3⅜, D 7¼. (A bill for the above items, submitted to Miss Grant from Richard Thelwell, No. 2 St Anns Square, Manchester, 31 March 1834, in the possession of the church, shows:

1	2 Quart flagon	£29 – 12 – 6
1	16in. Salver Glory edge	23 – 15 – 0
2	pint Chalices gilt inside	15 – 5 – 0
1	round bason	8 – 8 – 0
Engraving long inscription on the above		5 – 15 – 6
		82 – 16 – 0
	Disc.	4 – 3 – 0
		78 – 13 – 0

The bill is receipted 30 April 1834 'by cash 78 – 0 – 0')

In addition to the above are two *plates*, London 1871, makers 'J, E, W & J Barnard'. D 7. [197]

(166) RAWTENSTALL, Goodshaw Chapel (Baptist). *Cups*: pair, pewter, bowl with everted rim, short base and two moulded bands between a pair of handles. Unmarked, 18th-century. H 4, D 4⅜, W 6¾. *Plates*: pair, pewter. Touch of John Brown (C.639), early 18th-century. D 9⅛. [203]

The following items, of electroplate on Britannia metal, were probably added after the church removed in 1864 to a new chapel on Burnley Road [205]: *Cups*: pair, no handles. Late 19th-century. H 7¾, D 3⅞. *Flagon*: Inscribed 'PRESENTED to The Baptist Church GOODSHAW by Joseph White Esq. 1867'. H 13¾.

(167) SALFORD, Broughton Park (Congregational). (Plate 31) All items are inscribed 'Presented to the Broughton Park Congregational Church by Henry Lee and Thomas Rymer October 4th 1874'. Birmingham 1874, makers Elkington & Co., Manchester. *Cups*: four, of chalice form with small hemispherical bowl on tall stem with knop and quatrefoil base. H 8, D 4⅝. *Flagon*: spherical body with enriched band, on quatrefoil base, tall neck with spout, lid and angular handle. H 12. *Plates*: four, with broad enriched rim, D 9.

In addition a set of 13 trays of individual communion glasses, by Townshends Ltd, Birmingham, is dated '5 / 4 / 1905'. [234]

(168) TOCKHOLES, Bethesda Chapel (Congregational). Base metal set probably acquired 1803 when the chapel was built. *Cup*: plain bowl with moulded rim, hollow stem with centre band and hollow base. H 8, D 4. *Flagon*: short tapered body with moulded centre band, wide moulded base, domed lid, hollow handle and curved spout. H 8½, D base 6⅞. *Plates*: pair, with slight upstand at base. D 9. [238]

(169) WARRINGTON, Cairo Street (Presbyterian/Unitarian). *Cups*: (Plate 10A) two, of matching shape, tapered bowl rounded above tall baluster stem and broad flat base. (i) Engraved with crest of a stag in a thicket, trace of an erased name to left, later inscription '*The Giver G : P | A Gift to yᵉ protestant Dissenters | Chappell Warrington*'. London 1735, maker's mark in shield-shaped indent 'A.B mullet below'. H 10, D 3⅝. (ii) Faint traces only of erased inscription, none of crest, later inscription as above but '*The Giver J.B ... Protestant ...*'. Hall marks illegible, maker's mark in T-shaped indent with crown above, 'a lion rampant below T M'. H 9¾, D 3⅞. *Plates*: pair, pewter. Touch of Samuel Duncumb (C.1466), 18th century. D 9¼. [254]

LEICESTERSHIRE

(170) KIBWORTH HARCOURT (Congregational). *Plates*: pair, pewter. Initials 'W M' on base. Touch of Birch & Villiers of Birmingham (C.430), c. 1800. D 9⅝. Also base metal set of two two-handled *cups*, *flagon*, pair of *plates* and a *footed plate*, all inscribed 'CONGREGATIONAL CHURCH K.H. 1870'. [43]

(171) LEICESTER, Great Meeting (Presbyterian/Unitarian). *Cups*: (Plate 13B) eight, tapered bowl with moulded rim, swept stem and base, two tall handles. Inscribed '*Belonging to the* GREAT MEETING *LEICESTER* 1786'. London 1786, maker Robert Hennell. H 6½, to handles 7, D 4¼, W 7¼. (The cost of the cups, £38 3s., was met by voluntary subscriptions; a Vestry meeting of 5 June 1786 agreed 'that Mr J. Nutt and Mr J. Goode should wait on the Congregation, in order to raise a sum to purchase Plate for the Communion service'.) *Plates*: eight (i–iv) base metal. Inscribed 'Great Meeting Leicester. 1824'. D 10⅞. (A church minute of November 1824 is said to have ordered 'six handsome plates of the best silver to be bought of Mr Alcock' and to bear the above inscription) (v–viii) three. Inscribed 'Presented to the Great Meeting, Leicester 3rd April 1900'; one inscribed 'this service of four communion plates was presented to the Great Meeting Leicester April 3rd 1900 by Alfred Paget, Edwin Clapham, T. Fielding-Johnson, William Raven, E. Franklin Cooper'. London 1899, maker 'PE & Sons'. D 10. [44]

(172) LEICESTER, Charles Street (Baptist). *Plate*: pewter. Stamped initials 'C over I K'. Touch, a coronet with arm holding a spear, London label and 'hall marks' with initials 'S H' (C.5681). D 9¾. Also a two-handled *cup* and *flagon* in Britannia metal, by James Dixon. [46]

(173) LUTTERWORTH, George Street (Congregational/URC). *Plate*: pewter. 'Hall marks' of Joseph Giddings (C.1858), early 19th-century. D 9¼. [58]

LINCOLNSHIRE

(174) ALFORD (Congregational). *Cups*: pair, Sheffield plate, two handles. Maker N. Smith & Co., late 18th-century. H 5½, D 4, W 7½. *Plates*: pair, pewter with later plating. D 9⅜. [2]

(175) BOSTON, Spain Lane (Unitarian). *Cup*: base metal on petaloid base. Late 19th-century. H 9. *Plates*: pair, base metal. Late 19th-century. D 9. [Evans (1897) 27, lists a *cup* of Sheffield plate with two handles. H 6] [44]

(176) GAINSBOROUGH, Beaumont Street, later Trinity Street (Presbyterian/Unitarian). *Cups*: three, each with everted rim, small upstand at base, and pair of barbed handles. (i) Plain bowl inscribed 'I⋅F' for ?John Flower. London 1691, maker 'S H linked'. H 3¾, D 4⅛, W 6¾. (ii) Gadrooned lower half, inscribed below rim '⋅H | EA | 1697' for ... Hopkinson. London 1695, maker 'SL in monogram, on shield'. H 3¾, D 4¾, W 7¾. (iii) Plain bowl, inscribed on base 'E⋅H' for ?Elizabeth Hopkinson. London 1718, maker Matthew Lofthouse. H 4¼, D 4⅝, W 7½. *Plates*: pair, pewter. Touch of Thomas Bacon of London (C.181), mid-18th-century. D 9¼. [96]

(177) KIRKSTEAD, Abbey Chapel (Presbyterian, later Anglican). *Cup*: beaker with short tapered body and slightly everted rim. Inscription on side 'F over H I' for ?Henry and Jane Fines, with scrolled ornament and scratching on underside 'LT'. London 1658, maker 'NS

in shield between two mullets'. H 3⅜, D rim 3⅝, base 2¾. *Dish*: shallow bowl enriched with pattern of eight conjoined circles, on squat trumpet-shaped base. London 1653, maker 'R F over cinquefoil in heart-shaped die'. H 1½, D 4½. [Now in Lincoln Cathedral Treasury]   [159]

(178) LINCOLN, High Street (Presbyterian/Unitarian). *Cups*: pair, base metal, plain bowl on stem with knop. 19th-century. H 7⅝, D 3¾. *Plates*: pair, pewter. Touch, arm holding spear, issuing from a crown, London label and 'hall-marks' with 'S H' (C.5681), late 18th-century? D 9⅝.   [168]

(179) STAMFORD, Barn Hill (Wesleyan Methodist). A base metal set includes *Cups*: with cylindrical bowl above hollow stem with moulded band. Early 19th-century. *Flagon*: with domed lid, spout and scrolled handle. Mid-19th-century. (The congregation also has an unusual set of three, formerly four, tall two-handled glass *love-feast cups* with engraved decoration. H 8⅛.)   [240]

NORFOLK

(180) BRISTON (Independent/Congregational). The church meeting jointly at Briston and Guestwick held plate from both sections of the church; the following are claimed to belong to Briston. *Cups*: two (i) (Plate 1B, C) bowl, inside gilt, with S-shaped sides enriched with alternate banding and formal foliage, oval cartouche at front with faint traces of initials, two handles with serpent-head lower terminals, inside base enriched with repoussé decoration. London 1658, maker's mark 'a crosier between G S in shield' for ?Gilbert Shepherd. H 2⅛, to handles 2¼, D 3¼, W 5¼. (ii) similar in style, date and maker to last but not gilt inside. Cartouche inscribed '.B. | .W.M.' H 2¼, D 3⅜, W 5¼. [both cups reported sold since 1972] (See also (184) below)   [19]

(181) BROOKE, High Green (Strict Baptist). *Cups*: pair, base metal, bowl with band of ornament below rim, short moulded base and two strap handles. Inscribed on face '1798' within shield and similarly on back 'W C'. Maker I. Vickers. H 4¾, D 4, W 7⅜. *Plates*: pair, base metal with central foot. Inscribed 'W C' within shield. Maker I. Vickers, *c*. 1798. H 3¾, D 8¾.   [22]

(182) GREAT YARMOUTH, Old Meeting-house (Independent/Unitarian). Prior to the division of the church *c*. 1731 and the formation of the New Meeting the plate comprised thirteen silver beakers, two silver tankards, one silver flagon, seven pewter plates and six candlesticks. These were divided between the two sections of the church (Clowes (1912) 69–71), the Old

Meeting retaining six beakers, two tankards, four pewter plates and three candlesticks.

[When G. E. Evans recorded the plate of the Old Meeting in 1894 (Evans (1897) 260–2) it comprised the following: *Cups*: six beakers, H 6¾, D 3⅞, all with straight tapered sides and without distinct bases (i) 'richly chased floral design', a drawing shows a band of interlace ornament below the rim with pendant floral ornament. Inscribed '1638 | I H'. London? 1631. (Cripps (1926/1967) 108, possibly referring to cups i–ii, quotes instead a Norwich assay for 1637, maker's mark 'TS linked' for ?Thomas Skottoe. This may also be the 1638 beaker said by Jackson (1921) 317 to be then in the Pierpoint Morgan collection). (ii) 'richly chased design, of different pattern to above'. Inscribed 'S | G E', date letter worn. (iii) plain. Inscribed 'M | S + A'. London 1705. (This and the next two dates may result from confusion between the London date letters for 1654 and 1705; the earlier date was quoted by Jackson (1921) 125 for beakers from Great Yarmouth, maker ?Richard Neale, which may be these). (iv) plain. Inscribed 'W + B'. London 1705. (v) plain. Inscribed 'T + L'. London 1705. (vi) plain. Inscribed 'The Gift of John Arnold and Margarett, his wife', date letter worn. *Plates*: pewter, two, plain. D 11. The six beakers from the Old Meeting were sold *c*. 1900 'to defray a debt on the chapel', Jones (1905–6) 374. The fate of the other items is unknown]   [88]

(183) GREAT YARMOUTH, Middlegate Street (Congregational/URC). Following the division in the church the New Meeting received seven silver beakers, one silver flagon, three pewter plates and three candlesticks. Of these only the beakers remained in 1906, to which replicas of each were then added.

[*Cups*: (Plate 2A) seven 'beakers' (i) slightly flared rim and projecting base, band of interlace decoration below rim with entwined floral decoration. Inscribed 'E. T'. Marks illegible, ?early 17th-century. H 6⅜, D 3¾, base 3½. (ii–vii) plain with everted rim and plain projecting base. Severally inscribed 'W B; M D; T C; T L; C | I E; D S'. London 1654, maker's mark 'T B' in monogram. H 5½, D 4, base 3¾. All the above items were sold in 1926 and the proceeds expended on the purchase of a manse]

Surviving items recorded in 1972 were *Cup*: one, replica of 1652 beaker. London 1905, maker Crichton Bros. H 5⅜, D 4. *Plates*: seven, electroplate. Inscribed below 'C C' for Congregational Church.   [89]

(184) GUESTWICK (Congregational). The church meeting jointly at Briston and Guestwick held plate from both sections of the church; the following were claimed to belong to Guestwick. *Cups*: two (i)

(Plate 19A, C) bowl with slightly everted rim and small upstand at base, two handles with head terminals on top, bowl engraved with chinoiserie decoration of oriental trees and birds. Inscribed with initials 'A W' below base. London 1683, maker's mark 'R' for ?Alexander Roode. H 3⅛, to handles 3¼, D 4⅛, W 6⅝. (ii) plain bowl with everted rim and slight upstand at base, two slender barbed handles. Inscribed 'M ✻ W' below base. London 1689, maker 'SL' in monogram. H 3⅜, D 4⅛, W 6⅝. *Plates*: pair, pewter. Inscribed with initials 'G over E I'. Touch of Timothy Fly (C.1704), early 18th-century. D 9⅛. *Flagon*: Sheffield plate, with spout, handle and lid. Early 19th-century. H 12⅜. (See also Briston (180) above) [96]

(185) NECTON (Baptist). *Plate*: pewter. Touch of Henry Little (C.2948), mid-18th-century. D 9¼. [141]

(186) NORWICH, St Mary's Plain (Baptist). *Cups*: four (i–ii) pair, with plain bowl, everted rim, on hollow stem with centre band and moulded base. Scratched on base 'W, 1746'. London 1746, maker Thomas Whipham. H 8¼, D 3⅞. (iii–iv) pair, copies of last in shape and size, London 1816, maker William Bateman senr. [formerly in Hungate Museum, Norwich] [160]

(187) NORWICH, Old Meeting-house (Congregational). *Cups*: (Plate 8A) set of six tall standing cups, plain bowl on baluster stem and moulded base. Bowl inscribed '✻The Gift of Mr B. Balderston to yᵉ Congregational Church | in NORWICH 1757'. London 1757, maker 'J W' for ?John Wirgman. H 10, D 4½. *Plates*: five (i) moulded rim and three short moulded feet. Inscribed underneath 'The Property of the | Congregational Church | in NORWICH 1757'. London 1757, maker T.M for ?Thomas Moore. H 1½, D 10⅛. (ii–v) electroplate, plain. Uninscribed. Late 19th-century. D 10⅛. *Flagons*: pair, Sheffield plate, plain tapered body, moulded base, spout, handle, domed lid. Inscribed below spout 'OLD MEETING | NORWICH | 1860'. H 14. [152]

(188) NORWICH, Octagon Chapel (Presbyterian/ Unitarian). *Cups*: (Plate 13A) set of four, inside gilt, sharply tapered bowl on flared stem and beaded base, two tall reeded handles rising high above rim and separate cover with beaded flange and leaf-bud finial. London 1785, maker's mark 'B.M' in rectangular sinking. H 7¼, to handles 9, top of cover 10¾, D 4⅝, W 7¾. *Plates*: six, moulded rim. Centre inscribed in monogram 'C J P F' and date 1713 below, scroll added above inscribed 'THE ‖ GIFT ‖ OF ‖ Mᴿ ‖ IOHN ‖ RAINING'. London 1713, maker Seth Lofthouse. D 9. [formerly in Hungate Museum, Norwich] [159]

(189) SWAFIELD, Bradfield (Congregational). *Cup*: (Plate 1D) one (formerly two, see Browne (1877) 314) S-shaped bowl with short upstand at base, and two S-shaped handles of circular section. Bowl inscribed 'The Gift of Mr C. Robins 1737', on underside scratched date 1678. London 1677, maker's mark 'H E'. H 2⅝, D 3⅜, W 5⅞. *Flagons*: two, pewter, with straight-sided body on coved base, double-curved handle and domed lid with thumb rest, no spout. Inscribed 'C Robins | 1737'. H 10¾, 11. [Plate now at North Walsham [148]] [203]

(190) THARSTON, Hapton Chapel (Presbyterian/ Unitarian). *Cups*: pair, plain beaker-shaped bowls with cable-moulded lower border on trumpet-shaped stem and base. Inscribed below base 'G G' for George Gay. London 1670, maker's mark 'in a shield RH a cinquefoil and two pellets below'. H 3⅞, D 2½. *Plate*: moulded rim. London, late 17th-century (Evans (1897) 100–1, claims 1670), maker's mark ? 'BT'. D 10. [Now at Castle Museum, Norwich] [209]

NORTHAMPTONSHIRE

(191) RINGSTEAD (Baptist). *Cups*: pair, base metal, bowl with everted rim on hollow stem with moulded band and spreading base, two double-curved handles. Bowl engraved with oval cartouche inscribed 'The Gift of T. R 1787'. H 6⅞, D 3⅞, W 6¾.

(192) ROADE (Baptist). *Cups*: four, base metal. 19th-century. H 7⅞. *Flagon*: by Dixon, 19th-century. *Plates*: three, pewter. (i) Touch of Samuel Smith of Snow Hill, London (C.4379), after 1728. D 8⅞. (ii) Touch of Edward Toms (C.4770), late 18th-century. D 9¼. (iii) Touch of Thomas King (C.2752), after c. 1676. D 9⅜. [55]

NORTHUMBERLAND

(193) ALNWICK, St James, Pottergate (Presbyterian/ URC). *Cups*: six, plated base metal (i–ii) pair, bowl with everted rim, moulded band, short stem and base, two handles with scrolled terminals. Bowl inscribed 'Pottergate Congregation | (Alnwick) | 1795'. (iii–iv) pair, no handles. Inscribed 'St James, Presbyterian Church Alnwick 1886'. H 7¼, D 4. (v–vi) pair. Inscribed, in circle, 'L P C | 1879' for Lisburn Presbyterian Church (Relief Church, Lisburn Street, Alnwick). *Flagons*: three (i–ii) pair, pewter, straight-sided tapered body with central band, handle, spout and flat lid. Stamped inside base with crowned rose 'Made in Edinburgh'. 18th-century. H 9⅜. (iii) base metal, part set with cups v-vi above and similarly inscribed. H 11½. *Plates*: three pairs. Two inscribed 'St James Presbyterian Church Alnwick 1913'. D 10. *Alms-dishes*: six,

pewter (i) much decayed. Rim 1½ wide inscribed 'HEB XIII 16 LUKE 12 33 REMEMBER THE POOR 1689'. H 2¼, D 12¼. (ii) Uninscribed. D 15. (iii) D 13¼. (iv–vi) D 15. [10]

(194) BAVINGTON, Great Bavington (Presbyterian/ URC). *Cups*: (Plate 6B) two (i) slightly tapered bowl on baluster stem and broad base. Bowl inscribed '*the Gift of:G⁎M:To:H⁎C*' (GM is believed to relate to the MIDDLETON family of Belsay). London 1655, maker's mark 'IC' or 'I G' with mullet below. H 6⅝, D 4. (ii) generally similar to last but straighter sides to bowl. Inscribed as above. London 1658, maker's mark a bird or martlet. H 6½. D 3⅞. *Flagons*: (Plate 25B) pair, pewter, straight-sided tapered body with centre band, moulded base, slender handle, no spout, flat lid. Inscribed inside lids in crowned letters 'G B C'. Touch inside base of George Lowes of Newcastle upon Tyne (C.3001), pre-1765. H 10¼. *Alms-dish*: pewter. Inscribed 'E B' (crowned). D 15. [14]

(195) BERWICK-UPON-TWEED, Wallace Green (Presbyterian). *Cups*: two (i) Sheffield plate, plain bowl with everted rim, on stem with knop. Inscribed 'Protestant Dissenting Congregation Tweedmouth 1797'. H 9¼, D 5. (ii) plated base metal, slender bowl on swept stem and base, one double-curved handle. Bowl engraved with 'IHS' in sunburst. Early 19th-century. H 8⅛, D 3¾, W 5½. [24]

(196) BERWICK-UPON-TWEED, St Aidans, Church Street (Presbyterian). Plate includes *Alms-dishes*: two, pewter. Early 19th-century. D 16½. [25]

(197) BERWICK-UPON-TWEED, High Meeting, High Street, later St Andrew's, Greenside Avenue (Presbyterian Church of Scotland). [Four *cups* and four *flagons* were purchased during the ministry of James Williamson (1768–76) (Scott (1888) 370). Unlocated] [26]

(198) BLYTH, Waterloo Road (Presbyterian/URC). *Cups*: three, pewter (i) straight-sided bowl on stem with knop and spreading base. Bowl inscribed '*The property of the dissenting* | CONGREGATION at BLYTHE | Anno Domini 1777'. Touch, inside bowl, of Tidmarsh of London (C.4739–45), late 18th-century. H 7⅛, D 2⅞. (ii–iii) tapered bowl on stem and flat base. Bowl inscribed 'BLYTH MEETING'. H 7¾, D 3½. *Flagon*: (Plate 25C) pewter, straight-sided body with moulded base, handle and domed lid with finial, no spout. Inscription and maker as cup i. H 13¼. *Plate*: pewter. Marks unidentified, late 18th-century. D 13½. Other items comprise one plain *cup*, three two-handled *cups*, two *flagons* and two *plates*, all late 19th-century. [29]

(199) CHATTON (United Presbyterian). *Flagon*: base metal, straight-sided tapered body with moulded rim, middle band and base, large hollow handle, spout and domed lid. Body inscribed 'CHATTON | UNITED PRESBYTERIAN CHURCH | CONGREGATED 1ST JULY 1850 | REV. DAVID YOUNG | ORDAINED OCT. 1851'. Makers Shaw & Fisher, Sheffield. H 12. [In URCHS Collection]

(200) FALSTONE (Presbyterian/URC). *Cups*: four, pewter, narrow bowl on stem with knop and moulded base. Bowl inscribed '*For the Congregation of* | FALL-STONE | *1769*'. Touch, inside bowl, of Tidmarsh, London (C.4739–45). H 7, D 2⅞. *Flagons*: (Plate 25D) four, pewter, straight-sided body with moulded upper band and base, no spout, double-curved handle and domed lid with finial. Inscription as on cups. H 13½. *Plates*: two, pewter. One with London label and shield-of-arms. D 9⅜. *Alms-dish*: pewter. Inscribed on back 'FOR THE CONGREGATION OF FALLSTONE'. D 20½. *Basin*: pewter. Unmarked. H 2, D 9⅛. [34]

(201) FORD, Etal (Presbyterian). *Flagons*: pair, pewter, slightly concave sides to body, spreading at base, with moulded centre band, no spout, handle and flat lid. Body inscribed 'THE PROTESTANT DISSENTING | CONGREGATION AT ETAL 1767'. Touch, inside bottom, of William Hunter of Edinburgh (C.2473), c.1767. H 8½, D base 6¼. *Dishes*: pair, pewter. Unmarked. H 2⅛, D 14⅝. [In URCHS collection. Paper labels record 'Pewter Communion Plate (found in right hand cupboard 1927) Etal Presbyterian Church'] [37]

(202) HALTWHISTLE (Presbyterian). *Cups*: (Plate 11A) pair, pewter, shallow hemispherical bowl with broad rim and moulded band, on hollow baluster stem and moulded base. Bowl inscribed 'THE UNANIMOUS PURCHAS OF THE PROTESTANT | DISSENTING CONGREGATION AT HALTWHISTLE | MR IOHN WARDIN MINISTER 1745'. H 7⅝, D 5¾, depth inside bowl 2⅞. [In URCHS collection] [39]

(203) HARBOTTLE (Presbyterian). *Cups*: (Plate 11C) pair, pewter, plain bowl with everted rim, on hollow baluster stem and moulded base. Bowl inscribed '*H + C 1766*' (for Harbottle Congregation). H 8½, D 5¾. [In URCHS collection] [40]

(204) INGRAM, Branton (Presbyterian/URC). *Cups*: four, base metal, bowl with everted rim on short stem and base, two large handles with heart-shaped lower terminals. Bowl inscribed '*THE PROPERTY OF THE* | *Presbyterian Congregation* | *at Brampton* | NORTH-UMBERLAND | 1810'. Maker I. Vickers. H 7, D 4¾, W 9. *Flagons*: two, base metal, tall cylindrical body with centre band, moulded base, spout, handle and

domed lid. Inscribed as cups. Maker I. Vickers. H 5. *Plates*: two, pewter. Inscribed on rim 'Mary Bolam 1824 Donary'. Touch of Robert Sadler of Newcastle upon Tyne with false London label (C.4088). D 13½, 15. *Baptismal basin*: base metal. Inscribed as cups. H 4¾, D 10. [All the plate from Branton was reported sold *c.* 1979] [50]

(205) NEWCASTLE UPON TYNE, Brunswick Chapel (Wesleyan Methodist). *Cup*: Base metal, plain bowl on stem with knop. H 7½, D 4. (reputed to come from chapel at Kingswood, Glos.) [62]

(206) NEWCASTLE UPON TYNE (Presbyterian/ Unitarian). [A set of plate sold in the late 19th century 'in part payment of a modern service' is said to have been inscribed ' … Dr Richard Gilpin, Pastor, 1693' (Evans (1897) 182)]

(207) STAMFORDHAM (Presbyterian). *Cups*: pair, base metal, S-shaped bowl with everted rim, moulded base and two double-curved handles. Uninscribed. 19th-century. H 4⅝, W 8⅜. *Plate*, pewter. Touch of William Hogg of Newcastle upon Tyne (C.2367), late 18th-century. D 15. *Dish*: pewter. Inscribed with crowned initials 'R S'. Touch of George Lowes of Newcastle upon Tyne (C.3001), pre-1765. H 2, D 14¾. [In URCHS collection, deposited 1953] [71]

NOTTINGHAMSHIRE

(208) NOTTINGHAM, Friar Lane, later George Street (Baptist). *Cups*: four, of similar design, bowl with everted rim, centre band, on short stem and moulded base, two handles. (i) Inscribed 'BAPTIST CHURCH | Frier-Lane | NOTT:^M'. London 1773, maker John Deacon. H 5¼, D 4, W 7. (ii) As last except 'Friar' in inscription. H 5¼, D 4⅛, W 7⅛. (iii) Inscribed as first. London 1792, maker John King. H 5⅜, D 4, W 7¼. (This cup was bought 9 January 1793 from Mr Lingford, silversmith and jeweller, Beastmarket Hill (Godfrey and Ward (1903) 15)) (iv) Inscribed 'BAPTIST CHURCH | George Street | NOTT^M'. London 1815, maker William Bateman. H 5¾, D 3⅝, W 6⅞. *Flagons*: pair, electroplate. Inscribed on silver insert 'BAPTIST CHURCH | George Street | NOTTINGHAM'. Late 19th-century. H 14¼–14¾. [Now in Castle Museum, Nottingham] [39]

(209) NOTTINGHAM, Castle Gate (Congregational). *Cups*: pair, bowl with everted rim, mid band, short stem and moulded base, two double-curved handles. Inscribed 'CASTLEGATE MEETING'. London 1759, makers William Shaw & William Priest. H 6, D 4¾, W 8¼. [41]

(210) NOTTINGHAM, High Pavement (Presbyterian/ Unitarian). *Cups*: three (i) plain bowl with middle band, short stem and base and two handles. Bowl inscribed 'THE GIFT OF ALEX^R BURDEN AL^D | TO THE HIGH PAVEMENT SOCIETY IN NOTTING^M : 1737'. London 1726, maker William Darker. H 4½, D 4⅛, W 7. (ii–iii) (Plate 15D) pair, interior gilt, bowl with everted rim, upper cable moulding, gadrooned lower half, on moulded base, with two barbed handles. Bowl inscribed on small round cartouche within scaled and scrolled surround '*Belonging | to the HIGH | PAVE-MENT | SOCIETY | NOTT^M*'. London 1752, maker Fuller White. H 4¼, D 4½ , W 6½. Also late 19th-century set of two two-handled *cups*, *flagon* and *plate*, plated base metal, engraved with 'IHS' in sunburst. [44]

(211) UPPER BROUGHTON (General Baptist). *Cup*: Sheffield plate, plain bowl with centre band, on short stem and base, with two handles. Maker W. Smith & Co., late 18th-century. H 5½, D 3⅜, W 6⅝. [59]

OXFORDSHIRE

(212) ALVESCOT (Strict Baptist). *Plate*: pewter, broad rim engraved with shield-of-arms. Touch of Jonas Durand (C.1475), early 18th-century. D 9¾. [1]

(213) ASTON BAMPTON AND SHIFFORD, Cote (Baptist). *Cups*: two (i) (Plate 12B) plain two-handled bowl with centre band on moulded base. Bowl inscribed '*The Gift of Joseph Morse of Stow to the | Society of Protestant Dissenters Meeting at | Coat Oxon, for the Use of the LORDS-SUPPER. 1774.*', scratched weight '12oz: 15: 12' on underside. London 1734, maker Francis Spilsbury. H 5½, D 4⅝, W 8. (ii) early 19th-century replica of last, Sheffield plate. Uninscribed. H 5¼, D 4⅝, W 8½. *Flagon*: plated base metal. By R. Broadhead & Co., late 19th-century. H 10¼. *Plates*: three, pewter (i) with initials on underside 'B over W E'. Touch of Burford & Green (C.698), *c.* 1748–80. D 9¼. (ii–iii) pair. With initials on (ii) 'W:M | I:E | S:T | E:T | S:S'; on (iii) 'S:T | 1791'. London label, late 18th-century. D 8⅞. [6]

(214) HOOK NORTON (Baptist). *Plates*: (Plate 26D) pair, pewter. Rim engraved within pecked oval 'Hooknort | B : Church' and on one the figure '17' (? Incomplete date). Touch of John Shorey (C.4263), early 18th-century. D 10⅞. Also a two-handled cup and a flagon, electroplate, late 19th-century. [57]

(215) OXFORD, New Road (Baptist). Plate includes two tall flagons (? plated) inscribed 'Oxford Meeting 1814. the gift of Mrs M. Collingwood'. [76]

RUTLAND

No plate has been recorded from this county

SHROPSHIRE

(216) BROSELEY, Old Chapel (Baptist). *Cups:* two (i) bowl with cable moulding between pair of handles, lower half gadrooned, slight upstand at base. Inscribed below rim '*The Gift of DOCT^R J. W. PERROTT to the Baptist Church in Broseley. 1763*', scratched number '2813' below base. London 1703, maker Nathaniel Lock. H 3½, D 4¼, W 6¼. (ii) (from former Birch Meadow chapel, Broseley) base metal, part of a set comprising two cups and flagon, now dispersed. Plain bowl on stem and base. Number '2819' on base. Mid-19th-century. H 7⅝, D 3¾. *Plate:* pewter. Touch of John Duncumb (C.1465) with false London label, 18th-century. D 9½. [8]

(217) LUDLOW, Old Street (Congregational). *Cups:* two (i) bowl with slightly everted rim, upper cable moulding between two handles, lower part gadrooned, slight upstand at base, plain oval cartouche on one face in scrolled surround. Inscription below base '*The | Gift of Mary Reed | for ye Use of ye Meeting | at Ludlow | 1744*'. London (Britannia) 1703, maker Humphrey Payne. H 4¼, D 4⅝, W 8⅛. (ii) (Plate 16A) bowl with everted rim, cable moulding between pair of strap handles, coarse gadrooning to lower half and short upstand at base, plain rococo cartouche at front. Later inscription below base '*Presented by Mr James Hockey, | to the Independent Church, Ludlow, 1859.*'. London 1768, maker's mark '—S / — R'. H 4⅝, D 5, W 7¼. *Flagon:* electroplated Britannia metal. Inscribed below base '*Independent Church, | Ludlow. by John Evans. | 1854*'. Makers James Dixon & Sons. H 11¼. *Plates:* pair, pewter. Inscribed on underside '*Ludlow Meeting*'. 'Hall marks' resemble (C.5725), *c.* 1780. D 9¼. [50]

(218) NEWPORT, Wellington Road (Congregational/URC). *Cup:* glazed pottery, straight sides and pair of handles, moulded base broken away. Light blue background with gilt decoration ornamented on front with sprig of 'forget-me-not' and scroll inscribed 'Do this in Remembrance of Me', rear decorated with fern leaves. H 4, D 4⅝, W 7⅛. [60]

(219) OSWESTRY, Christ Church (Congregational/URC). [The following are reported to have been sold 1922–3. *Tankard:* straight sides with moulded rim and base, one hollow handle and flat hinged lid, front engraved with shield-of-arms of Lloyds of Montgomeryshire. Chester 1690–92, maker Ralph Walley (Cripps (1926) 112; Jones (1905–6) 284, Pl.X). *Cups:* three (i) two-handled gadrooned cup. London 1709, maker Nathaniel Lock. (Cripps (1926) 262) (ii–iii) two 'George III' cups. *Plate:* footed plate, London 1702.] [68]

(220) SHREWSBURY, High Street (Presbyterian/Unitarian). *Cups:* (Plate 10D) pair, tall bowl with everted rim, hollow stem with knop and moulded base. Inscribed within large oval panel with decorative border '*Donum | I S | Huic Ecclesiae | ex Residuo | Bonorum Dom^i | IOH^S BRYAN | 1735*'. London 1735, maker Humphrey Payne. H 8⅝, D 4. (John Bryan died 1699, the cups were bought with the residue of his legacy) *Plates:* pair, Sheffield plate by Prime of Birmingham, 19th-century. [88]

(221) SHREWSBURY, Swan Hill (Congregational). *Cups:* pair, plain bowl with everted rim on hollow stem with centre band and moulded base. Late 19th-century inscription 'SWAN HILL CHAPEL' added beneath. London 1777, maker Thomas Wallis. H 7⅝, D 3⅝. *Flagon:* Sheffield plate, tall cylindrical body on moulded base, handle and domed lid with anthemion thumb rest. Later inscription below as on cups. *c.* 1840. H 13¾. *Plates:* five, pewter. Initials below 'N M' for ?New Meeting. Touch of three leopards' heads (C.6046) unidentified, *c.* 1770, with ?false London label. D 9⅝. [89]

(222) SHREWSBURY, Abbey Foregate (Congregational/URC). *Cup:* electroplate, inscribed 'Congregational Church 1874'. H 8½, D 4. [91]

(223) WEM URBAN, Noble Street, Wem (Presbyterian). [*Cups:* silver, one inscribed 'The gift of the Rev. Mr Holland, to the Dissenting Chapel in Wem, 1752', said to match one 'given two years previous' by Mrs Bassnett (Elliott (1898) 64). Unlocated] [108]

(224) WEM URBAN, Chapel Street, Wem (Independent/URC). [*Cups:* four, silver plate on copper, with plain bowl, stem and base, together with a *flagon*; reported sold in 1970] [109]

(225) WHITCHURCH URBAN, Dodington, Whitchurch (Presbyterian). [*Alms-dish:* pewter, with inscription added 'This Ancient Almsdish, used in the Presbyterian Chapel, Dodington, lost in 1843, was recovered and given to the Trustees for use in the Church of the Saviour, Whitchurch, by the Rev. George Eyre Evans, 1893'. D 15. (Evans (1897) 256) Unlocated] [113]

SOMERSET

(226) BATH, Trim Street (Presbyterian/Unitarian). *Cups:* pair, bowl with S-shaped sides, moulded base and two double-curved handles. Engraved with a rococo cartouche enclosing monogram '*J C*' and surrounding inscription '*For the Use of the Meeting in*

Frog-lane BATH 1744'. London 1744, maker John Swift. H 4⅝, D 3½, W 6¾. *Plates*: pair, with shaped hexagonal edge and three short feet. Engraved and inscribed as cups. London 1744, maker Robert Abercromby. H 1⅝, D 10. [7]

(227) BATH (Moravian). *Cup*: plain bowl with reeded rim, stem, moulded base and two handles. Secondary inscription on bowl, 'Unitas Fratrum | Bath | 1765–1918'. London 1803, maker's mark 'T H'. [Now at Moravian Chapel, Lower Wyke, Yorks., WR. (see (344) below)] [19]

(228) BRIDGWATER, Dampiet Street (Presbyterian/Unitarian). *Cups*: pair, bowl with upper cable-moulded band between two handles, gadrooned lower half, small upstand at base. Inscription below rim 'A. W. | *1692*', also secondary inscription added below base '*Christ Church Chapel | Bridgewater*' (sic). London 1692, maker's mark 'I Y, a horse between'. H 4⅛, D 5¼, W 8½. *Plates*: pair, plated base metal. Inscribed as cups with date 1849. D 9.

[The above cups were bought by the trustees in 1755; another cup, now missing, bought in 1753, was engraved with the arms of Robert Blatch (Evans (1897) 31–2). Evans also reports (*UHST*, IV (1929) 282) that in place of a flagon the church possessed 'a remarkably handsome purple glass decanter with stopper of Bristol make'] [30]

(229) CHARD, South Chard (Independent/Strict Baptist). *Plate*: pewter. Touch of Ash & Hutton of Bristol (C.118), *c*. 1760. D 9⅜. [45]

(230) CREWKERNE, Hermitage Street (Presbyterian/Unitarian). [Evans (1897) 62, reports *Cups*: two mugs. ?London 1701. H 4, D 3. Unlocated] [58]

(231) ILMINSTER, Old Meeting, East Street (Presbyterian/Unitarian). *Cups*: two beakers (i) (Plate 3B) cable moulding below rim, moulded base, side ornamented with repoussé floral decoration. Inscribed close below rim 'M D | 16 71'. Norwich *c*. 1670, maker's mark 'I.E, star between two mullets below', in heart-shaped indent. H 3½, D 3⅛. (ii) (Plate 3C) splayed rim and moulded base, narrow gadrooned upper band and deeper band of gadrooning to lower half of bowl. Exeter 1701, maker J. Elston. H 3½, D 3⅛. *Tankard*: (Plate 22A) interior gilt, S-shaped sides, moulded base, handle and domed lid. Elaborately enriched with floral decoration and cartouche on one side enclosing secondary inscription '*Presented to the | Congregation of the Old Meeting | for the Lords Table | by MARY COLLINS of Ilminster | 12th May 1849.*' London 1770, maker 'T S' for Thomas Parr. H to rim 7, to lid 8½. *Plates*: two, electroplate, late 19th-century. D 9. [87]

(232) KINGSBURY EPISCOPI, Middle Lambrook (Congregational/URC). *Cup*: Sheffield plate, bowl with everted rim, hollow stem with knop and swept base closed below. Inscribed around edge of base '*Revd S. R. Pittard to Lambrook Meeting*'. Early 19th-century. H 9⅛, D 4½. *Plate*: pewter. Initials 'M V' on base. Touch of Hall & Scott (C.2089), early 19th-century. D 9¾. *Christening basin*: rose bowl with gadrooned base and swag ornament. Inscribed 'F.E.H. | *Middle Lambrook | Meeting | 1956*'. London 1905, maker 'R.P'. H 3⅝, D 5½. [92]

(233) SHEPTON MALLET, Cowl Street (Presbyterian/Unitarian). *Cup*: shaped bowl on short stem and moulded base, two double-curved handles with leaf ornament. Bowl inscribed '*The Gift of Wm Provis | the Younger to the Congregation. | Cowl St Chapel | Shepton Mallet.*' London 1799, maker 'S H' for Solomon Hougham. H 5⅜ D 3¾, W 7¾. *Plate*: on central hollow foot and moulded base, inscribed as above. London (Britannia) 1710, maker Nathaniel Lock. H 2½, D 9⅝, base 3¾. [136]

(234) SOUTH PETHERTON, Old Meeting, Palmer Street (Presbyterian). *Cups*: two beakers (Plate 3D) (i) bowl with slightly concave sides and moulded base, enriched with band of repoussé floral decoration below rim. London 1691, maker's mark 'a goose or duck'. H 3⅜, D 3⅛. (ii) bowl with moulded base, band of formal decoration below rim, lower half enriched with acanthus leaves. London (Britannia) 1697, maker William Andrews. H 3⅜, D 2⅞. [Plate now in Taunton Museum. See also *CHST* III (1907–8) 25–6; *ProcSA* XII (1887–9) 170; *Som A&N H Soc* LXVIII (1922) xcii] [145]

(235) TAUNTON, Mary Street (Baptist/Unitarian). *Cups*: (Plate 10A) four, plain bowl on tall hollow stem with knop and flared base. Bowl inscribed '*The Gift of Mr Samuel Noble Attorney at Law of Taunton to the Baptist Meeting of that Place | 1744/5*'. London 1746, maker Humphrey Payne. H 9, D 3⅞. *Plates*: three (i–ii) pair, with slightly raised centre. Inscribed around rim as cups. London 1746, maker possibly John Cafe. D 10⅜. (iii) inscribed (a) on rim 'F | .I.E. | 1688'; (b) below rim 'M : : F | 1739'; (c) around rim '*The Gift of Miss Ann Atkins of Taunton unto the Trustees of the Chapel in Mary Street in that Town to be used at the Sacrament. 1818*'. London 1688, maker's mark ? 'G C intertwined'. D 9⅜. *Flagons*: (Plate 23B) pair, tall with straight sides, moulded band above spreading base, handle and domed lid. Inscribed on front as cups. London 1746, maker Humphrey Payne. H 11¾.

Also here, property of the Western Union, are *Cups*: pair, Sheffield plate, inside gilt, with stem, flared base and two handles. Inscribed underneath '*Devon and Cornwall Unitarian Missionary Society*'. Early 19th-century. H 5⅞, to handles 6½, D 3⅞. *Plate*: pewter. Inscribed as last. Touch of S. Cocks (C.1004), after 1819. D 9⅝. [153]

(236) TAUNTON, Paul's Meeting (Congregational/URC). *Cups*: six (i) (Plate 7C) with tapered bowl on baluster stem and wide base. London 1634, maker's mark 'C.L, cinquefoil below'. H 7¾, D 4⅛. (ii) bowl with S-shaped sides, short upstand at base and two handles, bowl decorated in repoussé with flowers and foliage, a peacock and a turkey. Inscriptions (a) below rim 'T over R M'; (b) '*Jan ye 1st | 1668*'. London 1667, maker's mark 'R D mullet below'. H 4, to handles 4¼, D 4. (Cup said to have been given by Rollin Mallock who also gave the site for the meeting-house in 1688). (iii) bowl with everted rim, upper cable moulding between two handles and gadrooned lower half. Oval cartouche in scrolled surround inscribed '*The | Gift of | Jno: Cole | to Pauls | Church*', scratched on base '*1732*'. London 1703, maker Nathaniel Lock. H 3⅝, D 4⅜, W 7. (iv) two-handled gadrooned cup, as last but coarser in detail. Cartouche inscribed '*1713 | The Gift of | Eliz^{th}: Coles | Daug^{tr}: of Jos | Way*', scratched weight on base '*12:5*'. London 1705, maker's mark 'H ...' possibly 'H I, mullet above and below', for William Hinton; H 4½, D 5, W 8. (v) plain bowl on short stem and base, moulded band between two handles. Inscribed '*The Gift of Robert Clitsome | 1736*'. London 1736, maker 'R B in octagonal stamp' for Richard Bayley. H 6, D 5⅛, W 8½. (vi) similar to last but inscribed '*The Gift of Ann Clitsome | 1751*'. London 1750, makers William Shaw & William Priest. H 6⅜, D 5, W 9. *Flagons*: pair, Sheffield plate, straight-sided foliated body with base, spout, handle and lid with finial. Inscribed on base '*Presented | to the | Church assembling at Pauls Meeting, | Taunton, | by Mrs John Smith of | Leycroft House | January 1841*'. Also a set of six plates, electroplate, D 10, and three sets of Individual communion glasses, two dated 28 April 1907. [154]

(237) TRUDOXHILL (Congregational). *Cup*: plain straight-sided bowl with everted rim. Short upstand at base and two reeded handles. Front inscribed '*Trudox Hill Meeting*', rear engraved with 'IHS' in sunburst. Assay, possibly secondary, on base ring, London 1802, maker 'AE' or 'AF'. H 4½, D 3⅞, W 7¼. *Plate*: pewter. Inscribed 'TRUDOXHILL MEETING'. Touch possibly Yates, Birch and Spooner of Birmingham (C.5349), *c*.1800. D 9⅛. [163]

(238) WINSHAM (Congregational/URC). *Cups*: two, Sheffield plate, plain straight-sided bowl with lip and

thin gadrooned band below, on stem and reeded base. Early 19th-century. H 5⅞, D 3⅜. [186]

(239) YEOVIL, Vicarage Street (Presbyterian/Unitarian). *Cup*: plain bowl with everted rim on hollow stem with moulded band and base. Face engraved with 'IHS' in sunburst. London 1798, maker 'R B'. H 8⅝, D 4⅛. *Plate*: with central foot and moulded base. Engraved as above. London 1724, maker Nathaniel Gulliver. H 1⅞, D 5⅜. *Flagon*: Sheffield plate, bulbous body with insulated handle, lid and spout. Engraved as last. 19th-century. H 7¾. [198]

STAFFORDSHIRE

(240) DUDLEY, Old Meeting-house (Presbyterian/Unitarian). *Cups*: pair, plain bowl with everted rim on short stem and moulded base, two hollow handles. Inscribed '*GIVEN | For the Use of Dudley Meeting | by M^r I * F | 1751*' (?John Finch). London 1751, maker Benjamin Cartwright. H 6½–6⅝, D 4⅛, W 7. *Flagon*: Plated base metal, tapered body, with moulded base, handle, spout and domed lid. Inscribed below spout '*Old Meeting House | DUDLEY | 1853.*', scratched on underside 'Hy Ws Co | Quart | L | LH' (for Henry Wilkinson & Co. Sheffield). H 10⅝. *Plate*: plated base metal, with central foot. Inscribed as flagon. H 3¾, D 9⅛. [31]

(241) NEWCASTLE-UNDER-LYME, Old Meeting-house (Presbyterian/Unitarian). [Evans (1897) 183–4, records *Cup*: two-handled gadrooned cup. Uninscribed, similar in style to the 1703 cup from Matthew Henry's Chapel, Chester (see (22) above). London 1721. H 3½, D 4] [68]

SUFFOLK

(242) BECCLES, Hungate (Congregational/URC). *Flagons*: two, electroplate, inscribed 'INDEPENDENT CHURCH BECCLES 1868'. [Two silver *cups*, inscribed with the names and initials of Francis Haylock and Edmund Artist, deacons, and dated 1690 (Rix (1837) 153–4), are reported to have been sold *c*.1926] [8]

(243) BUNGAY, Upper Olland Street (Congregational/URC). *Cup*: tapered body, stem and base. Bowl engraved with band of Greek key ornament below rim. London 1796, makers Peter & Ann Bateman. H 6¼, D 3⅜. [23]

(244) BURY ST EDMUNDS, Churchgate Street (Presbyterian/Unitarian). Set of four *cups* (Plate 8B), plain bowl with everted rim, hollow stem with moulded band and moulded base, and four *plates* with moulded rim. Inscription on underside of plates '*St Edm^{ds} Bury*'. All items London 1711, maker Humphrey Payne. *Cups*:

H 7½–7¾, D 3¾–4; *Plates*: D 9¼. [Noted as in the care of the civic authorities. Although dating from the erection of the chapel this set was formally given to the trustees in 1720; it then also included two *flagons*, possibly pewter, each weighing about 7 lbs, which were sold in 1747.]   [25]

(245) BURY ST EDMUNDS, Garland Street (Baptist). *Cups*: two, base metal, with two handles. Early 19th-century.   [26]

(246) COWLINGE, Mill Road (Congregational). *Plates*: two, pewter. Touch 'Compton, London' in sunburst. D 10.   [39]

(247) FRAMLINGHAM, Old Meeting (Presbyterian/ Unitarian). *Cups*: two, tin glazed earthenware, each with a pair of handles, possibly for communion use. (i) white earthenware with blue transfer chinoiserie decoration. H 4¾, D 4½, W over handles 8. (ii) plain. H 4⅞, D 4⅝, W 7⅜. *Plates*: four, pewter. Three with touch of Timothy Fly (C.1704), early 18th-century.[48]

(248) HALESWORTH, Quay Street (Congregational/ URC). *Cups*: (Plate 4A) set of three beakers, with slightly tapered body and plain everted rim. London 1763, makers Thomas Whipham & Charles Wright. H 4⅜–4½, D 3½. *Flagon*: Sheffield plate, short tapered body with moulded band, base with wooden infill, spout, handle and domed lid, engraved below spout with foliage decoration. *c*.1800. H 7¾. *Plates*: pair, pewter. Stamped on base 'R over I F'. Touch of Thomas Powell (C.3750) and label of 'Eames' (?C.1490), *c*.1700. D 9½. [Some of these items may have belonged to the Independent Meeting at Walpole [149]; two beakers are reported sold since 1973]   [62]

(249) HAVERHILL, Old Independent (Congregational/URC). *Cups*: three, plated base metal, plain bowl on swept stem and base. *c*.1800.   [67]

(250) IPSWICH, St Nicholas Street (Presbyterian/Unitarian). *Cups*: four, each with two barbed handles (i) (Plate 14B) plain bowl, straight sides rounded below, with gadrooned decoration to lower third over slight moulded base. Inscribed below with initials 'C over WE, EW' and weight '10=18'. London 1691, maker's mark 'SH linked, in oval frame'. H 4¼, D 4¾, W 7½. (ii) (Plate 19B, D) bowl of like shape but with overall engraving of oriental trees, fountain, and within a wreath a shield-of-arms 'below a chief indented ermine, three griffins heads erased and crest of the same'. On underside 'A L' and weight '14=4'. London 1695, maker's mark 'R.C on dotted circle'. H 4. (iii) plain sides rounded to moulded base. Bowl inscribed '*The Gift of* | MARY BEAUMONT | *Jan^ry*. 13th. *1786*.', and on underside '∗M∗B∗ and weight '9=2'. London

1703, maker's mark 'K E mullet below in shaped indent' for William Keatt. H 4, D 4¼, W 6¾. (iv) upper band of cable moulding between handles, gadrooned lower third. Oval panel in cartouche inscribed 'EX DONO | .M.T.', scratched weight on underside '9=0'. London 1708, maker Richard Green. H 4¼. *Plates*: two (i) with wide rim. Engraved with shield-of-arms 'on a fess between three crosses saltire two and one three lions heads couped' marked below with weight '18=00' altered to '17=9'. London 1663, maker's mark 'RN with mullet below'. D 10⅞. (ii) rim with moulded edge. Engraved with shield as last but smaller, and scratched weight '15=6'. London 1682, maker's mark 'R or PR in cypher'. D 10⅞.   [76]

(251) IPSWICH, Tacket Street (Congregational/URC). *Cups*: three, each with two barbed handles, cable moulding between handles, gadrooned lower third and short upstand at base. (i) (Plate 14C) Cartouche inscribed '*The Gift of* | *Stanley West* | *Esq of London* | *To the Church* | *Under the Care* | *of the Rev^d M^r* | *Wm Notcutt* | *1725*.' London 1701, maker John Smithsend. H 3⅞, D 4⅞, W 7½. (ii) Generally similar to last but inscribed '*The Gift* | *of a Friend* | *To the Church* | *Under the Care … 1725*'. London 1704, maker Richard Green. H 4, D 4⅝, W 7. (iii–iv) pair, replicas of i and similarly inscribed. London 1729, maker 'G S' for ?Gabriel Sleath. H 3⅞, D 4⅞, W 7¾. *Flagons*: pair, electroplate by James Dixon & Sons. Inscribed '*Presented to the Independent Church, Tacket Street, Ipswich, by E. Goddard 1873*'. H 12.   [77]

(252) RENDHAM (Congregational). *Cups*: five, Sheffield plate (i–ii) (Plate 4D) plain bowl with moulded rim and base without handles or stem. Inscribed '*1650* | *Rendham* | *1757*'. 'Hall marks' include initials '*I M*', a standing figure, and a fleur-de-lys, *c*.1757. H 5½, D 4⅝. (iii–v) plain bowl on stem with centre band and base. Inscribed on edge of base '*Rendham 1840*'. H 8½, D 4. *Flagon*: plated base metal, tapered body on moulded base, thick handle, spout and lid with finial. Late 18th-century. H 12. *Plates*: five (i–ii) pair, Sheffield plate. Inscribed as cups i–ii. *c*.1757. D 9⅛. (iii–v) Sheffield plate. Inscribed as cups iii–v. *c*.1840. D 10.   [127]

(253) WATTISFIELD (Congregational). ['The valuable communion plate of the church part of which was presented as early as 1678' (*CHST* III (1907–8) 256) is reported to have been sold]   [153]

(254) WICKHAMBROOK (Congregational/URC). *Plates*: four, pewter. Inscribed on underside '*Wickhambrook Meeting*'. Touch of Hellier Perchard (C.3611), early 18th-century.   [158]

(255) WRENTHAM (Congregational/URC). *Flagon*: pewter, with tapered body, moulded rim, upper band and coved base, double-curved handle, spout and lid with finial. Circular inscription below base '*Revd Mr Townsends Meeting Jamaica Row Rotherhithe Road*' (Southwark, Greater London). Late 18th-century. H 13¾, D base 6½. *Plates*: four (i–ii) pewter, pair with cinquefoil rim. Inscribed below as on flagon. Touch of John Townsend (C.4795). D 9½. (iii–iv) pewter, pair. Touch of Timothy Fly. [The church formerly possessed two cups, 'given *c.*1650 by Francis Brewster of Pyes Hall and bearing the arms of Brewster'. These were sold *c.*1970]   [168]

SURREY

(256) ALBURY, The Apostles' Chapel (Catholic Apostolic). *Chalices*: pair, inside gilt, small plain bowl, sides splayed, on hexagonal stem with knop and 6-foil base. Birmingham 1851, maker 'E T & B'. H 8½, D 3⅞. *Flagons*: two (i) oval 6-foil body with handle, spout, lid surmounted by cross finial and moulded base. London 1831, makers Joseph & John Angel. H 14. (ii) plated base metal, bulbous body engraved 'IHS', handle and lid. Mid-19th-century. H 11. *Plates*: two (i) on central foot. Engraved with 'IHS' in sunburst surmounted by cross, inscribed below 'CATHOLIC CHURCH, ALBURY'. London 1838, maker Robert Garrard. D 6⅞, H 2. (ii) without foot. Engraved and inscribed as last. London 1840, maker Robert Garrard (Garrards). D 10. *Bowl*: formerly used as small alms-dish, ? silver. Hexagonal bowl on three feet, 19th-century. H 2⅜, D 6½.
                                                                    [1]

(257) CHARLWOOD, Providence Chapel (Calvinistic Independent). *Cups*: pair, plated, with two handles having heart-shaped terminals. Mid-19th-century. H 5½, D 3⅜, W 7. *Plates*: pair, pewter. Touch of Thomas Compton (C.1063). D 9¾.   [6]

(258) FARNHAM (Congregational/URC). *Cup*: glass mug with moulded rim, gadrooned or fluted lower part on moulded base, one handle. Reputedly used for communion in early days of the church (formed 1792). Late 18th-century. H 4, D 2¾.   [22]

(259) GODALMING, Mill Lane (Friends). *Plate*: pewter. Rim with initials 'S over I H'. Touch of 'Baldwin' (C.210–3). D 8½.   [27]

(260) HASLEMERE, Lower Street (Congregational). [Pannell (1908) 15, illustrates two pewter plates from the first chapel, built 1804]   [33]

(261) LINGFIELD, Dormans Land (Baptist). *Cups*: pair, electroplated Britannia metal, two handles. H 8⅜, D 3½, W 6¾. *Flagon*: material as last. By James Dixon

& Sons. H 14¼. *Plates*: pair, pewter. Touch of Compton (C.1063). D 9¾.   [40]

SUSSEX

(262) BATTLE, Mount Street (Baptist/Unitarian). [Evans, (1897) 12, lists an electroplate set of two *cups*, a *flagon* and two *plates*]   [5]

(263) BILLINGSHURST (General Baptist/Unitarian). *Cups*: pair, bowl with everted rim, base and two handles. London, maker 'I K' for ?Jasper Kelly or John Kidder (*cf* similar but larger cups at Horsham (269) below). H 2¾, D 2¼, W 4¼. *Flagon*: plated base metal, ewer-shaped body with engraved ornament, narrow neck with spout and lid, S-shaped handle. Late 19th-century. H 11¾ overall. *Plates*: two, pewter. With initials 'I K' on rim for James Knight (deacon), bought in 1780 for 6*s.* 7*d.* (church records). Touch of Richard Yates (C.5344). D 13¾.   [9]

(264) BRIGHTON, New Road (Baptist/Unitarian). [Evans (1897) 34, lists: *Flagon*: with 'handle, knob, lid and beak'. Inscribed 'Presented to the Rev. Robt. Ainslie by J. H. G. Marzetti for the use of the Communicants at Christ Church, New Road'. London 1867. H 8⅛. (Reported to be by Edward Barnard (A.E.)) Also two *cups* and two *plates*, silver plate on copper.]   [15]

(265) CHICHESTER, Eastgate (General Baptist/Unitarian). *Cups*: pair, bowl with moulded rim, short stem and moulded base and two hollow handles. London *c.*1751–5. H 4¼. *Plates*: four, pewter (i–ii) pair. Touch of R. Hitchman (C.2341), mid-18th-century. D 11. (iii) Touch of William Bartlett (C.279). D 13⅜. (iv) As last but touch illegible. D 13⅜. [The cups and two plates were reported stolen from Essex Hall, London, 1971]
                                                                    [24]

(266) CHICHESTER, Baffins Lane (Presbyterian/Unitarian). [Evans (1897) 47, records two two-handled *cups* with S-shaped sides and repoussé decoration including a lion and a unicorn. London 1668. (i) H 4¼, D 6, weight 13oz. (ii) H 4¼, D 5, weight 8oz 15dwt. Also two pewter *plates*, D 13. The dates of the cups are given in Jones (1905–6) as 1668 and 1676. The cups are reported to have been sold by the trustees in 1930] [25]

(267) CHICHESTER, Providence Chapel (Calvinistic Independent). [Reynolds (1961) records two pewter communion cups, one flagon with spout and two pewter plates 'crested with a dolphin entwining an anchor']   [26]

(268) CUCKFIELD (Baptist). [The church is said to possess a communion cup from Zion Chapel, New Cross Gate, Lewisham]   [34]

(269) HORSHAM, Worthing Road (General Baptist/Unitarian). *Cups*: set of four, bowl with everted rim, base and two strap handles. London 1781, maker ?Jasper Kelly or John Kidder. H 3⅜, D 3, W 5¼. *Flagon*: electroplate, 'bought by subscription about 1870'. *Plates*: pewter. (i–ii) Touch of Francis Whittle (C.5121), early 18th-century. D13⅜. (iii–iv) Touch of Richard Yates (C.5344), late 18th-century. D 13⅜.   [56]

(270) LEWES, Westgate (Presbyterian/Unitarian). [Pewter *plates* of *c*.1690 by Stephen Bridges, *cups* of Britannia metal in use from 1863 to 1914, and two *cups* of 'old Sheffield plate', given in 1914, are reported. Some of these items were stolen in 1970]   [67]

(271) LEWES, Jireh Chapel (Calvinistic Independent). *Cups*: pair, pewter, bowl with everted rim and moulded upper band, on stem with knop and shaped base. Early 19th-century. H 7¾, D 3⅞. *Flagon*: pewter, tapered body with moulded band and base, spout, domed lid with finial and shaped handle. Early 19th-century. H 12. [All reported stolen since 1971].   [64]

(272) WISBOROUGH GREEN, Zoar Chapel (Calvinistic Independent). Base metal set comprising two cups, flagon and two plates, by James Dixon & Sons. Inscribed 'Wisborough Green Chapel Novr 18th 1859'.   [105]

WARWICKSHIRE

(273) BEDWORTH, Old Meeting-house (Congregational/URC). *Cup*: lustreware, with two handles. H 6, D 4¼, W 6⅜ (damaged). *Plates*: three, pewter. Two by 'Duncumb', one with touch of Birch & Villiers (C.430). D 9½.   [10]

(274) BIRMINGHAM, Old Meeting-house (Presbyterian/Unitarian). [Evans (1897) 18, records four two-handled *cups*. London 1787. H 5¾; two *flagons*. London 1787. H 13¼; and four *plates* inscribed 'Old Meeting Church, Birmingham, 1885'. London 1885, given by Prime & Son at the rebuilding of the chapel. Unlocated]   [13]

(275) BIRMINGHAM, New Meeting-house (Presbyterian/Unitarian). *Cups*: four, bowl with false bottom, moulded rim and two hollow handles, on short stem and base. London 1782, maker Hester Bateman. H 6½, D 4⅝, W 8. [In Birmingham Art Gallery. Evans (1897) 19–20, also records four *plates*, Sheffield plate, by Wilmot & Roberts. D 6¾; and four *alms-dishes*, by Yates, Birch & Spooner. D 10½.]   [14]

(276) COVENTRY, Great Meeting-house (Presbyterian/Unitarian). [*Cups*: four, plain bowl with everted rim on hollow stem with centre band and moulded base. London 1731. H 7½. Reported sold *c*.1972. (See Jones (1905–6) 374)]   [29]

(277) COVENTRY, Cow Lane (Baptist). *Cup*: bowl with everted rim, narrow band between two tall reeded handles, on swept base. Inscribed in oval 'B.S.C.L.| Coventry | 1805'. London 1804, maker 'GB overstamping TW', for ?George Baskerville. [now in Coventry Museum and Art Gallery]   [30]

(278) HENLEY-IN-ARDEN (Baptist). *Cup*: Birmingham 1863, maker 'H M'. H 8, W 3¾. *Flagon*: Same assay and maker as cup. H 12¾.   [45]

(279) WARWICK, Castle Hill (Baptist). ['Two pieces of plate, a silver tankard and silver cup' were bequeathed to the Church under the will of Thomas Hurd, a tailor of Castle Street, dated 7th March 1681. Ivimey IV (1830) 540]

WESTMORLAND

(280) KENDAL, Market Place Chapel (Presbyterian/Unitarian). *Cups*: pair, pewter, bowl with band, hollow stem with knop and moulded base. Mid-18th-century. H 8, D 4. *Plate*: pewter. D 9⅜.   [10]

(281) STAINTON (Congregational/URC). *Cup*: bowl with narrow band between two handles, over moulded base. Engraved on face with initials and date 'T W | M F | 1733'. Newcastle 1732, maker Isaac Cookson. H 5, D 3⅞, W 7¼. *Flagon*: by James Dixon & Sons, Sheffield, 19th-century.   [39]

WILTSHIRE

(282) BERWICK ST JOHN, Ebenezer Chapel (Baptist). *Plate*: pewter. Touch of ?Bush & Perkins (C.740), late 18th-century. D 9¼.   [7]

(283) BRADFORD-ON-AVON, St Margaret's Street (Congregational/URC). Plated base-metal set comprising *Cups*: pair, inside gilt. Marked on base 'W. G. Hallett'. H 8, D 3⅞. *Flagon*: Inscribed 'Congregational Chapel | Morgan's Hill Bradford | 1844' and on base 'W. G. Hallett | Bradford | Wilts'. H 16. *Plates*: pair. D 9.   [17]

(284) CALNE WITHIN, Calne (Baptist). *Cups*: mugs, pair, pewter, with later silver plating, gadrooning to lower third. Inscribed 'T ✳ C | 1710'. H 3⅛, D 3⅛, W 4½. *Plates*: pair, pewter. Inscribed 'T C | 1710'. 'Hall-marks' as (C.5845) but possibly by John Peters of Bristol (C.3635). D 12⅛. (These items are said (Marsh (1903)) to have been given by Mr Cue of Compton Bassett)   [33]

(285) CORSHAM, Pickwick Road (Congregational). *Plates*: pair, pewter. Touch of Edgar & Son, Bristol (C.1510), early 19th-century. D 9½.   [50]

(286) DEVIZES, Old Baptist Chapel (Baptist). *Cups*: pair, plated base metal, with two handles. Mid-19th-century. H 5¼, W 7. *Flagon*: of similar substance and date. [57]

(287) DEVIZES, St Mary's Chapel (Congregational/URC). *Cups*: (Plate 13D) pair, tapered body with swept stem and reeded base, two thin reeded handles rising above rim. Secondary inscription on front, added *c.*1870 'PRESENTED TO THE | Christian Church | ASSEMBLING IN ST MARY'S CHAPEL | DEVIZES | BY | Ann Elgar | Jany 25th 1790'. London 1799, maker 'J H' for John Harris or Joseph Hardy. H 9½ overall, D 4¾, W 7. *Plates*: two. Inscribed as above. London 1800, maker 'J H'. *Flagon*: (Plate 24C) Inscribed as the gift of George Elgar Sloper, January 1st 1870. Exeter 1869. H 12½. [60]

(288) GRITTLETON (Strict Baptist). *Cups*: mugs, two, base metal. Uninscribed. *c.*1800. H 4, D 2⅞. *Plate*: pewter. Stamped 'C G' for Grittleton Chapel. D 8¾. [70]

(289) HORNINGSHAM (Congregational/URC). *Cups*: mugs, pair, pewter, with moulded base and hollow handle. Stamped '½ pint' below rim and 'G' with circular inscription 'CITY | BRISTOL'. Touch of Edgar & Son, Bristol (C.1510), early 19th-century. H 4. *Flagon*: base metal with bulbous body, narrow neck, spout, lid with finial and handle. Maker 'James Dixon & Sons'. H 10¼. [77]

(290) LONGBRIDGE DEVERILL, Crockerton Green (Baptist). *Cups*: (i) mug, base metal, bowl with everted rim, short stem and moulded base, barbed handle. Late 18th-century. H 4¼, D 3¼. (ii) 'rummer' of thick coarse glass with plain bowl, on stem and base (in communion use 1970). H 5⅜, D 2⅞. [87]

(291) LYNEHAM, Providence Chapel, Bradenstoke (Calvinistic Methodist / Strict Baptist). *Cups*: two (i) (Plate 29A) thistle-shaped bowl on moulded stem and enriched base. Lower part of bowl elaborately decorated in repoussé with roses and acanthus leaves, the upper part having two cartouches, one blank, the other inscribed 'Presented by | James Hillier | TO THE BAPTIST CHURCH | of Marlborough | JULY 18, 1848'. London ?1833. H 6¾, D 4. (Transferred after closure of Marlborough Chapel in 1921). (ii) Plated base metal, two handles. Mid-19th-century. H 8⅛, D 4, W 7½. *Plates*: two (i) (Plate 26F) plated base metal, supported on three short legs. Elaborately enriched and inscribed 'PRESENTED BY | R. Price | TO THE BAPTIST CHURCH | of Marlborough | 1848'. D 9¾. (Transferred after closure of Marlborough Chapel in 1921). (ii) base metal, mid-19th-century. D 10¼. [88]

(292) MALMESBURY (Moravian). *Cup*: plated base metal, with two handles; bought for three pounds in 1840 and presented to the Church by James Montgomery, poet and hymn writer, uncle of the minister. H 10¼, D 4¾, W 8¾. [92]

(293) NEW SARUM, Fisherton Street, Salisbury (Congregational/URC). Plate includes *Plates*: four, plated base metal. Inscribed 'Scots Lane Chapel 1841'. D 10. [111]

(294) SOUTHWICK, Old Baptist Chapel (Baptist). *Cups*: two, plated, with two handles. *c.*1875. *Flagon*: plated, given 1875. *Plates*: two, pewter. Touch illegible. D 9¼. (Doel (1890) 60, records: 'December 1st 1791 — bought tablecloth for Lords Supper and two putor coops and two putor dishes for the same use, marked I.M., dated 1745 each of them, and a basket to hold them'. He further notes (p. 67) that a silver-plated communion service was presented in 1875) [131]

(295) TISBURY (Presbyterian/Congregational). *Cup*: mug with single handle and moulded base. Inscribed on handle 'A A | M A'. London 1717, makers' marks, on base William Gamble, on handle Charles Overing. H 3⅜, D 2¾. [140, 141]

(296) TROWBRIDGE, Conigre Chapel (General Baptist/Unitarian). *Cups*: (Plate 28D) four, small tulip-shaped bowl on stem with knop and moulded base. London 1822, maker 'R P' for ?Richard Pearce or Robert Peppin. H 6⅜, D 3⅛. *Flagon*: electroplate. Late 19th-century. H 10½. *Plates*: pair, as flagon. D 9⅛. *Alms-dish*: brass. Repoussé representation of the Temptation in the Garden of Eden, with surrounding inscription, repeated thrice 'CHWART:DER:INFRIDO'. Possibly Dutch, 15th-century. D 16½. [142]

(297) TROWBRIDGE, Tabernacle (Congregational/URC). *Flagon*: plated base metal. Inscribed 'For the use of the Tabernacle Church Trowbridge November 15th 1867'. H 12.

The Church also possesses a silver *baptismal basin* (Plate 27B) from the former Presbyterian chapel in Silver Street, Trowbridge [150]: bowl with gadrooned rim and similarly enriched base. Inscribed 'THE GIFT OF MR. THO^S JEFFERIES LONDON 1767'. London 1767, maker Edward Aldridge. H 4⅜, D rim 8⅝ base 4½. (See also *CHST* III (1907–8) 26). [146]

(298) TROWBRIDGE, Manvers Street (Wesleyan Methodist). *Cups*: two, plated. H 7⅜, D 4¼. *Flagon*: plated. H 11¼. All by J. Wolstenholme, Sheffield. [Now at the Tabernacle (297)]. [148]

(299) WARMINSTER, Old Meeting (Presbyterian/Unitarian). Set (Plate 22B–D) comprising two tankards,

one flagon and two plates, given by John Langley, 2 May 1790, and bearing his shield-of-arms. London 1789, maker 'T W' for ?Thomas Wright. *Tankards*: body with intermediate band and moulded base, broad handle and domed lid. H 8⅛ overall. *Flagon*: tall body on flared base with scrolled handle, spout and lid with pineapple finial. H 12⅝ overall. *Plates*: cinque-foiled rim with beaded edge, mark 'I Y' for ?James Young. D 9½. [152]

(300) WESTBURY. Old Meeting (Congregational/URC). [*Cups*: two, plain bowl on trumpet-shaped stem and reeded base. Inscribed on bowl '*Belonging to the old meeting* | WESTBURY, WILTS. | JUNE, 1806. | *C. Sloper: Pastor*' were acquired by Wiltshire Library and Museum Service in 1989 from a private owner. (*Reform*, December 1989, 21)] [156]

(301) WILTON (Congregational/URC). *Cups*: pair, plain bowl on short stem and base with two handles. Inscribed on bowl 'R. THRING'S GIFT | TO THE INDEPENDENT CHURCH | AT WILTON 1791'. London 1791, maker John King. H 5⅜, D 3⅝. *Flagon*: plated base metal. Late 19th-century. H 15. *Plates*: pair, as flagon. Inscribed on face 'C' (for Communion). [159]

WORCESTERSHIRE

(302) BEWDLEY (Baptist). *Cup*: bowl with everted rim, moulded mid-band and base, two handles. Inscribed on bowl '*Gift of Josiah Stockwell* | *to the Baptist Church at Bewdley*' and on one handle 'S | J ⁎ H'. London 1757, maker Benjamin Cartwright. H 4⅞, D 4, W 6¾. [1]

(303) BROADWAY (Congregational). *Plates*: two, pewter, marked with initials 'P over W E'. Touch of Allen Bright (C.574), mid-18th-century. D 8⅞. Also two *cups* and a *plate*, by James Dixon & Sons, late 19th-century, and a base metal *flagon*, mid-19th-century. [10]

(304) EVESHAM, Oat Street (Presbyterian/Unitarian). *Cup*: bowl with centre band, moulded base and two double-curved handles with heart-shaped lower terminals. Inscribed 'PRESENTED | *to the Communicants* | *in the Presbyterian Chapel Oat Street Evesham* | *by the family of the late Anthony New* | *1838*'. London 1747, maker Humphrey Payne. H 6⅛, D 4, W 9. *Flagon*: electroplate, with handle, lid and spout. Maker 'T.R.W.'. H 11¼. *Plates*: two, pewter. (i) Stamped with initials 'S over I E'. Touch of horse's leg issuing from coronet. D 9¼. (ii) Stamped 'T over R E' on rim. D 9¾. [16]

(305) HALESOWEN, Park Lane Chapel, Netherend, Cradley (Presbyterian/Unitarian). *Cups*: pair, Sheffield plate, bowl with everted rim on short stem and moulded base, two handles. Inscribed within oval frame '*Park Lane Chappel* | *Cradley* | *1796*'. H 5¾, D 4, W 7½. *Flagon*: plated base metal, tapered body with lower band, moulded base, handle, spout, domed lid. Inscribed below spout '*Park Lane Chapel* | *Cradley*'. Early 19th-century. H 12¼. *Plates*: five (i–ii) pair, plated base metal, with gadrooned edge and three small button feet. Inscribed '*Park Lane* | **Chapel** | *CRADLEY* | *1819*'. D 10. (iii–v) pewter. One inscribed with initials 'I / F ⁎ L'. Touch resembles Samuel Duncumb (C.1466). D 9–9¼. [20]

(306) KIDDERMINSTER BOROUGH, New Meeting-house, Church Street, Kidderminster (Presbyterian/Unitarian). *Cups*: three mugs (i) (Plate 21A) straight-sided bowl on moulded base, double-curved handle. Inscribed on front 'N.M / K' for 'New Meeting, Kidderminster' and on handle 'P / H E'. London 1721, maker Thomas Farren. H 4, D 3, W 4¾. (ii) similar pattern to last but simpler handle. Engraved on front with shield-of-arms *three beasts heads couped in chief* above two plain quarterings, initials above 'S R' and below 'N M / K'. London 1726, maker 'SL'. H 4½, D 3½, W 5½. (iii) (Plate 21B) baluster-shaped body on moulded base, double-curved handle with leaf ornament. Inscribed 'N.M / K'. London 1793, maker Charles Aldridge. H 4¾, D 3⅛, W 5¼. *Plates*: three, pewter. (i) Inscribed below 'Kidderminster New Meeting | 1782'. Touch resembles Samuel Duncumb (C.1466). D 11. (ii–iii) pair. Touch as last. D 9¼. [27]

(307) STOURBRIDGE, Lower High Street (Presbyterian/Unitarian). *Cups*: pair, plated base metal, plain bowl with everted rim and gadrooned lower edge, on stem with band and moulded base. Mid-19th-century. H 6, D 3¾. *Flagon*: plated base metal, tapered body on four scrolled feet, with shaped handle, pointed spout and lid with cross finial. Inscribed on front '*Presented to the Presbyterian Chapel, High Street, Stourbridge,* | *on the 6th July, A.D. 1888,* | *the one hundredth Anniversary of its erection* | To the Glory of GOD, | *and in affectionate memory of* | *Sarah, daughter of John Scott* | *and widow of Robert Scott of Stourbridge* | *who was born on the* 10th June, 1800, | *and died on the* 21st March, 1874.' *Plate*: plated, cinque-foiled rim with gadrooned outer edge. 19th-century. D 10. [41]

(308) WORCESTER, Sansome Walk (Baptist). Communion set 'given by Henry Page, minister, in 1821, in use until 1906', ?plated base metal, comprising *Cups*: four, thistle-shaped bowl, lower half gadrooned, on

trumpet-shaped stem. H 6½. *Flagon*: with gadrooned decoration on body. H 11½. *Plates*: five.   [52]

(309) WYTHALL, Dollox Chapel, Kingswood (Presbyterian/Unitarian). *Cup*: Sheffield plate, shaped bowl on moulded base, two handles with heart-shaped terminals. Front inscribed '*K W / M*' for 'Kingswood Meeting'. Early 19th-century. H 5⅛, D 3½, W 7. *Plates*: four, pewter. Inscribed below '*K W / M*'. Touch of Duncumb, late 18th-century. D 9⅜.   [58]

YORKSHIRE
YORK

(310) YORK, St Saviourgate (Presbyterian/Unitarian). *Cups*: pair, bowl with straight sides, spirally gadrooned below, on short moulded base, two S-shaped barbed handles. Inscribed on face '*C / T M*'. London 1694, maker's mark 'R G star above'. H 3¼, D 4½, W 7⅜. *Flagon*: vase-shaped octagonal body on swept base, with neck, spout, lid with small finial, and bent wood handle. London 1790, makers Peter & Jonathan Bateman. H 13¾ to finial, 14¼ overall. *Plates*: (Plate 26A) pair, with broad 2¼ rim and moulded outer edge. Inscribed below rim '*The gift of Andrew Taylor. 1696*'. London 1673, maker 'T.L in plain stamp'. D 10⅝.   [1]

EAST RIDING

(311) KINGSTON UPON HULL, Bowl Alley, Hull (Presbyterian/Unitarian). [Evans (*UHST* VII (1939–42) 69–70) records the following items *Cups*: two. Inscribed 'The gift of Ralph Peacock for the Use of the Chappell'. London 1723. *Flagon*: Sheffield plate. Inscribed 'The Gift of Henry Blundell for the use of the Unitarian Chapel, Bowl Alley Lane, Hull'. H 13½. *Plates*: (i) London 1685. D 10. (ii) Inscribed 'C. / L. K.'. Similar to last, but Hull assay, maker Thomas Hebden, late 17th-century. D 10. Reported sold *c.* 1976]

(312) THORNGUMBALD (Congregational). [*Cup*: plain bowl on tall stem and wide base. Inscribed 'Presented by | *Mrs I. F. BUTTER,* | *to the Congregational* | *Church,* | *Thorngumbald,* | *28th Jany 1849*'. After closure of the chapel the cup passed to Fish Street, Hull, and then after September 1982 to the URC church in Selby]

NORTH RIDING

(313) MALTON, Wheelgate (Presbyterian/Unitarian). *Cup*: 'The Popple Cup', Sheffield plate, inside gilt, plain bowl tapered down to stem and swept base, with simple angular engraving. *c.* 1800. H 6¼.   [83]

(314) MELBECKS, Low Row (Congregational). Base-metal set of two plain *cups*, two footed *plates* and

flagon, by Broadhead & Atkin of Sheffield. Cups and plates inscribed 'PRESENTED | BY | Mrs E. A. KNOWLES Senr | 1841'   [89]

(315) WHITBY, Flowergate (Presbyterian/Unitarian). *Cup*: plain bowl with moulded band and base, two handles. Inscribed on front '*The gift of Mr Leo Wilde for ye use of ye* | *Protestant Dissenters in Whitby* | *Feb 14 1732*', and on back 'W / L * M'. London 1718, maker John Wisdome. H 5¾, D 5⅜, W 8¾. *Plates*: pair. Inscribed below 'For the Use of the Protestant Dissenters in Whitby ye j May 1735'. Maker John Swift. D 9.   [151]

(316) YARM, Octagon Chapel (Methodist). *Cup*: Sheffield plate. Maker 'T H | & S'. H 7½, D 4. *Flagon*: Sheffield plate, spout, lid and handle. H 12½.   [156]

WEST RIDING

(317) ADDINGHAM, Chapel Street (Wesleyan). *Cups*: pair, plated, bowl with Greek key ornament, small knop on stem. Inscribed 'A C' conjoined, for Addingham Chapel. H 8, D 4. *Flagon*: plated. Inscribed as above. H 13.   [3]

(318) BRADFIELD, Underbank Chapel, Stannington (Presbyterian/Unitarian). *Cup*: plain bowl with everted rim, splayed foot, two reeded strap handles. Weight scratched on base '8=15'. London 1751, maker 'J B'. H 4, D 4¼, W 7⅛. *Plates*: four, pewter. (i) Inscribed 'S over S R'. (ii–iv) Inscribed on rim 'S over R S'. Touch of ?John Aughton (C.149). D 8⅞. *Communion cloth*: white linen, stitched inscription 'Stannington Chapel October 1st 1854'.   [52]

(319) BRADFORD, Chapel Lane (Presbyterian/Unitarian). *Cup*: bowl, interior gilt, with everted rim, upper cable-moulded band, gadrooned lower third, moulded base and two cast handles. Large oval cartouche inscribed 'I * D'. London (Britannia) 1703, maker Seth Lofthouse. H 5½, D 5¼, W 8.   [58]

(320) DONCASTER, Hallgate (Presbyterian/Unitarian). [Evans (*UHST* VI (1935–8) 152–3, records *Cup* and *cover*: similar to the cups from Baffins Lane, Chichester, so presumably with repoussé decoration, but with cover. 17th-century, maker's mark 'C.S. divided by an arrow'. Reported sold by trustees *c.* 1940–5]   [120]

(321) GISBURN FOREST, Tosside (Congregational). Base-metal set by Broadhead & Atkin of Sheffield, mid-19th-century, comprising *Cups*: pair, with everted rim, stem with central band and base. H 8¼, D 4⅛. *Flagon*: conical body with centre band, base, spout, domed lid and 'anticalorific handle'. 3 pints. H 10¼. *Plate*: on three short claw feet. D 9.   [139]

(322) GOMERSAL (Wesleyan Methodist). Late 19th-century set including two chalice-like *cups* and a *flagon* dated 1883.   [141]

(323) HALIFAX, Northgate End (Presbyterian/Unitarian). *Cups*: (Plate 13C) pair, tapered bowl on swept stem and base, two tall handles. Bowl inscribed '*THE GIFT OF* | *the Congregation* | *for the Chapel* | *at Northgate End* | *HALIFAX* | *1792*'. London 1792, maker Henry Chawner. H 6½, overall 7⅛, D 4, W 6¼. *Plates*: pair, pewter. Stamped 'R over C S'. Touch of James King (C.2741) but with 'hall marks' of Richard White (C.5097). D 9⅜.   [153]

(324) HALIFAX, Square Chapel (Congregational). *Cup*: electroplate, with two handles. Maker 'H W & Co'. H 8¾, D 4⅛, W 7¾. *Flagons*: pair, tall body with lower band and base, spout, handle and domed lid. London 1829, maker 'W B'. *Plates*: six, electroplate. (i–iv) Four marked as cup. D 9. (v–vi) Two plain. D 10.   [154]

(325) HALIFAX, Heywood Chapel, Northowram (Congregational/URC). [Four cups and a flagon, now in private hands, include *Cup*: base metal, two-handled bowl on stem with large centre band, mid-19th-century. H 7⅝]   [163]

(326) HARROGATE, Victoria Avenue (Congregational/URC). [Whitehead (1932) 260, refers to a communion service presented by Joseph Taylor of Leeds in 1847]   [174]

(327) HEPTONSTALL, Octagon Chapel, Northgate (Wesleyan Methodist). *Cup*: one of two cups given away by the trustees (minutes 10 April 1885) but later returned, is of base metal, bowl with everted rim, centre band, on stem and moulded base. Late 18th-century. H 7, W 3⅝.   [193]

(328) LEEDS, Mill Hill (Presbyterian/Unitarian). *Cup*: bowl with everted rim, centre band, on short stem and moulded base, two handles. Inscribed on front '*THE COMMUNION CUP* | *FOR MILL-HILL CHAPPEL*'. London 1718, maker Seth Lofthouse, but mark of Charles Overing on each handle. H 5¼, D 4¾, W 7⅞. [A second, identical, cup is said to be in private hands] *Flagon*: ?plated base metal, tapered body, domed lid and handle. H 10¾. *Plates*: two, pewter. Touch of John Shorey (C.4263). D 8⅞, 10⅞.   [260]

(329) LEEDS, Brunswick Chapel (Wesleyan Methodist). Set comprising two cups, a flagon, a footed plate and two plain plates, all discreetly inscribed 'WILKINSON, *AURIFEX*, LEEDS', Sheffield 1825. Makers S. Roberts, Smith & Co., of Sheffield (except flagon). *Cups*: (Plate 29C) pair, inside gilt, slightly everted rim, moulded band, rounded to stem with band and base.

Bowl inscribed within floral cartouche 'METHODIST | SOCIETY | Brunswick Chapel | LEEDS'. H 7¾, D 3⅞. *Flagon*: slightly tapered sides with moulded base, spout, domed lid with finial, and handle. Inscription on each side within cartouche '*THE* | *Sacramental-service con* | *-sisting of this Flaggon, two Cups* | *a Salver and two Plates with the* | *Pulpit is furnished by Ladies for* | *the use of the Methodist Society* | *worshipping at BRUNSWICK-CHAPEL* | *LEEDS, which was opened for Divine-service by the Revd George* | *Clark L.L.D the Revd George* | *Marsden, and the* | *Revd Jabez Bunting A.M* | *on September 9th 1825*.' Maker John & Thomas Settle, Sheffield. H 14, D base 7⅝. *Plates*: three. Inscribed as cups (i) with central foot. D 10⅞, H 2. (ii–iii) pair, without foot. D 9⅜.   [271]

(330) MORLEY, Old Chapel (Congregational/URC). *Cups*: two (i) bowl with everted rim, on short stem and base, two hollow handles with heart-shaped lower terminals. Inscribed 'J. REYNER | to Morley ['old' inserted] Chapel Society | 1766'. London 1765, maker 'W C' for ?William Cripps. H 6⅛, D 4¼, W 8½. (ii) similar style to last but thinner and with centre band on bowl. Enriched on one face with a shaped shield bearing a demi-lion rampant all within a garter, and on the opposite face a later inscription 'ST. MARY'S | Congregational Church | MORLEY'. London 1808, makers Peter & William Bateman. H 6½, D 4¼, W 7½. *Plates*: four (i) with 6-foil gadrooned edge and three short feet. Inscribed '*Presented to the* | *Christian Society* | *at* | *Morley old Chapel* | *by* | *Watson & Frances Scatcherd* | *A.D. 1803*'. London 1772, maker 'E.C.'. D 10⅛. (ii) as last but on three claw feet. Inscribed 'To the Glory of God | Presented by Henry Dykes | In Memory of His Father & Mother | Joseph & Mary Dykes | January 1908'. London 1906, makers Pierce & Sons, Leicester. D 10⅜. (iii) shape as last. Inscribed 'ST MARY'S CONGREGATIONAL CHURCH, | MORLEY, | November 1884'. Sheffield 1884, makers 'TB / JH' in shield. D 10⅛. (iv) Sheffield plate. 'IHS' with cross on upper face. Early 19th-century. D 9¼.

Also here is an electroplate set from Rehoboth Chapel, Morley, comprising two *cups*, a *flagon* and four *plates*, the last with inscribed date 1859; also an electroplated *plate* believed to come from St Mary's Mission.   [300]

(331) NEWTON, Newton in Bowland (Congregational). [*Cup*: pewter, bowl with everted rim, middle band, short moulded base and pair of double-curved handles. 'Hall-marks' include initials 'R.B', late 18th-century. H 4, D 4⅜, W 7¾. Plate: pewter. Two 'crowned rose' stamps beneath, maker unknown. D 9¼. Both these items were in private possession in 1974]   [310]

(332) PUDSEY, Fulneck (Moravian). *Cups*: three, ?plated, with moulded stem and base and two handles. One inscribed 'No 11 | BRETHREN'S CHAPEL | FULNECK | 1835'. *Baptismal basin*: electroplate, oval basin with two end handles.   [335]

(333) QUEENSBURY AND SHELF, Queensbury (General Baptist). *Cup*: electroplate, with two handles. Inscribed 'G. B. C. / Q' for General Baptist Church, Queensbury (or Queenshead). *Flagon*: electroplate. Similarly inscribed.   [336]

(334) SADDLEWORTH, Delph (Congregational). Set of Sheffield plate vessels. All inscribed 'Delph Independent Chapel 1852'. Comprising *Cups*: two, shaped bowl, gilt inside, on stem with knop. H 8½, D 4. *Flagon*: with hollow handle, spout and domed lid. H 10½. *Plates*: two. D 10.   [352]

(335) SELBY, St Michael's Chapel, Millgate (Presbyterian/Unitarian). *Cups*: two (i) bowl with everted rim, upper cable moulding, gadrooned lower part on slight upstand at base, and pair of cast handles, one repaired. Oval cartouche in crudely scrolled surround with date '1707'. Inscribed below rim '*The gift of Beatrix Bacon | to the Chappel of Selby*'. London 1706, maker Seth Lofthouse. H 4⅛, D 4¾, W 7¼. (ii) base metal, rounded bowl on stem with knop, moulded base and two handles. Circular infilling below base crudely inscribed 'The Gift | of | Ann and her husband, | James Beavington, | to St. Michael's Chapel, | Millgate, Selby, | August 8th, 1875 | George Jones | Minister'. H 7¾, D ¼. *Flagon*; electroplate, tapered body with spout, lid and insulated handle. Inscribed 'SELBY Unitarian Church'. H 11¼.   [365]

(336) SHEFFIELD, Upper Chapel (Presbyterian/Unitarian). *Cups*: two (i) bowl with upper cable moulding, lower part gadrooned, on plain base, two cast handles with beaded outer faces. Oval cartouche on front engraved with letters 'H ✳ N' between a bird in flight and another standing below; also modern scratching on base 'A D 1682 / 1705'. London (Britannia) 1706, maker Humphrey Payne. H 4⅝, D 5⅛, W 7⅝. (ii) (Plate 16c) bowl with shaped sides, upper cable moulding, lower part thinly gadrooned, base and two reeded strap handles. Cartouche on front with foliage surround, inscribed '*Sheffield | Up^r Chapel | 1785*'. London 1784, maker 'I. Y' for ?James Young. H 5, D 4⅝, W 8½.   [369]

(337) SHEFFIELD, Nether Chapel, Norfolk Street (Congregational). *Cup*: electroplate, plain bowl on stem with knop and base. Maker 'M W & S', late 19th-century. H 7⅜, D 3⅝.   [370]

(338) SHEFFIELD, Queen Street (Congregational). *Cups*: Pair, Sheffield plate, tapered bowl with moulded rim, swept stem and base, and two tall handles. Inscribed on two faces (a) 'This Cup | is the New Testament | in my Blood, | which is shed | for you | Luke 22.20'; (b) 'Given | to the INDEPENDENT CHURCH | Queen-street SHEFFIELD, | in the Year | 1787 | Jehoida Brewer, Minister'. H 7¾, overall 8⅞, D 5. *Plates*: four, pewter. All inscribed 'Queen Street Chapel 1787'. D 9¼.   [371]

(339) SHIPLEY, Saltaire (Congregational/URC). Electroplate set of *c.*1860, maker 'M H & Co', comprising *Cups*: pair. H 7¾, D 3¾. *Flagon*: with hinged lid, spout and handle. H 13. *Plates*: pair. D 9⅞. Also *Plates*: two, electroplate, by Fattorini & Sons. D 10.   [380]

(340) SOWERBY BRIDGE, Sowerby (Congregational). *Cup*: one of two, the other said to be in private hands, plated base metal, bowl on narrow stem and base, two handles. Inscribed around base 'Sowerby — 1874'. *Plates*: two, plated. Similarly inscribed. D 9. [398]

(341) SOWERBY BRIDGE, Bolton Brow (Wesleyan Methodist). *Plate*: electroplate, with central foot. Inscribed 'BOLTON BROW | IHS | Wesleyan Chapel'. Makers Walker & Hall, Sheffield. H 3¼, D 10.   [399]

(342) SOWERBY BRIDGE, Boulderclough (Methodist New Connexion). Lustreware set with silvered finish comprising *Cups*: two, shaped bowl on stem and base, two handles. Enriched with an illustration of the chapel and 'METHODIST NEW CONNEXION BOULDERCLOUGH CHURCH SOWERBY'. H 5½, D 4⅝, W 7½. *Flagon*: tapered body with spout, handle, and detached lid with finial. Enriched as cups. H 8¾ overall. *Plates*: two. Enriched as before. D 9¾.   [404]

(343) WAKEFIELD, Westgate Chapel (Presbyterian/Unitarian). Sheffield plate set comprising *Cups*: two, tapered bowl on moulded stem and base. H 8¼, D 3½. *Flagon*: Engraved with cross enclosing 'IHS'. H 13½. *Plates*: two, with central foot, narrow gadrooned edges. H 2¼, D 7⅞. (Evans (1897) 246, who wrongly describes the metal as 'pewter', claims that this set was bought 3 November 1777 for 4½ guineas)   [441]

(344) WYKE, Lower Wyke (Moravian). *Cup*: bowl with reeded rim on foot and base, with two handles. Later inscription on bowl 'Unitas Fratrum, Bath, 1765–1918'. London 1803, maker 'T H' for ?Thomas Hayter. *Dish*: electroplate. Inscribed 'Presented by the Sisters Taylor to the Moravian Chapel, Wyke, 1893'. D 10. *Baptismal basin*: (Plate 27D) electroplate, oval basin with two end handles. Late 19th-century. H 5¾, length overall 15¼.   [456]

BIBLIOGRAPHY

PRINCIPAL REFERENCES

Bowmer (1949–50) Bowmer, J. C., 'The Communion Plate of Early Methodism', in *WHSP XXVII* (1949–50), 102–08 [reprinted as Appendix II in next item]

Bowmer (1951) Bowmer, J. C., *The Sacrament of the Lord's Supper in Early Methodism* (1951)

Bradbury (1912) Bradbury, F., *History of Old Sheffield Plate* ..., Sheffield (1912 reprinted 1968)

Burns (1892) Burns, T., *Old Scottish Communion Plate* (Edinburgh, 1892)

Cotterell (1929) Cotterell, H. H., *Old Pewter its Makers and Marks: in England, Scotland and Ireland, an account of the Old Pewterer and his Craft* (1929). [referred to as 'C.' in lists]

Cripps (1891) Cripps, W. J., *Old English Plate ...* (4th edn 1891; reprint 1967 of 11th impression of 1926)

Evans (1897) Evans, G. E., *Vestiges of Protestant Dissent ...* (1897)

Evans (1927–40) Evans, G. E., 'Our Communion Plate and other Treasures' in *UHST* vols. IV–VII [covering Unitarian congregations in alphabetical order from Ainsworth to Liverpool]

Fallon (1972) Fallon, J. P., *Marks of London Goldsmiths and Silversmiths: Georgian Period (c. 1697–1837)* (1972)

Heal (1972) Heal, A., *The London Goldsmiths 1200–1800, a Record of the Names and Addresses of the Craftsmen, their shop-signs and trade cards* (1935, reprinted with altered pagination 1972)

Herdman (1901) Herdman, E. F., *Sacramental Tokens of the Presbyterian Churches in England* (Morpeth, 1901)

Jackson (1989) Jackson, C. J., *English Goldsmiths and their Marks ...* (1905; 3rd edn 1989, reprinted 2005)

Jones (1905–6) Jones, E. A., 'Some Old Silver Communion Plate of English Nonconformity', in *The Magazine of Fine Arts*, Vol. I (1905–6) 280–5, 371–4.

Oman (1934) Oman, Charles, *English Domestic Silver* (1934)

Oman (1957) Oman, Charles, *English Church Plate 597–1830* (1957)

Oman (1964) Oman, Charles, 'English Mediaeval Base Metal Church Plate', in *Archaeological Journal*, CXIX (for 1962) published 1964, 195–207

Stell (1986) [Stell, C. F.], *An Inventory of Nonconformist Chapels and Meeting-houses in Central England* (1986)

Stell (1991) Stell, C. F., *An Inventory of Nonconformist Chapels and Meeting-houses in South-West England* (1991)

Stell (1994) Stell, C. F., *An Inventory of Nonconformist Chapels and Meeting-houses in the North of England* (1994)

Stell (2002) Stell, C. F., *An Inventory of Nonconformist Chapels and Meeting-houses in Eastern England* (2002)

MINOR REFERENCES

Atkinson (1897) Atkinson, T. D., *Cambridge Described and Illustrated* (1897)

Browne (1877) Browne, John, *History of Congregationalism and Memorials of the Churches in Norfolk and Suffolk* (1877)

CHST *Transactions of the Congregational Historical Society* (from 1901)

Cleal (1908) Cleal, E. E., *The Story of Congregationalism in Surrey* (1908)

Clowes (1912) Clowes, J. E., *Chronicles of the Old Congregational Church at Great Yarmouth 1642 to 1858* (1912)

Densham & Ogle (1899) Densham, W. & Ogle, J., *The Story of the Congregational Churches of Dorset* (1899)

Doel (1890) Doel, W., *Twenty Golden Candlesticks! Or A History of Baptist Nonconformity in Western Wiltshire* (1890)

Elliott (1898) Elliott, Ernest, *A History of Congregationalism in Shropshire* (1898)

Godfrey & Ward (1903) Godfrey, John T. & Ward, James, *The History of Friar Lane Baptist Church, Nottingham* (1903)

Horne (1893) Horne, C. Silvester, *A Century of Christian Service: Kensington Congregational Church 1793–1893* (1893)

Ivimey (1811–30) Ivimey, Joseph, *A History of the English Baptists* (4 vols. 1811, 1814, 1823, 1830)

Marsh (1871) Marsh, John B., *The Story of Harecourt* (1871)

Marsh (1903)   Marsh, A. E. W., *A History of the Borough and Town of Calne* (*c.* 1903) Chap. XII, 168–179

Nightingale (1890–3)   Nightingale, B., *Lancashire Nonconformity* (6 vols. 1890–3)

Pannell (1908)   Pannell, C., *The Story of the Congregational Church at Haslemere, Surrey* (1908)

PHSJ   *Journal of the Presbyterian Historical Society of England* (14 vols, 1914–72)

ProcSA   *Proceedings of the Society of Antiquaries of London* (2nd ser., 32 vols, 1859–1920)

RCHM (1925)   Royal Commission on Historical Monuments (England), *An Inventory of Historical Monuments in London* (vol. II, West London, 1925)

Reform   *The Magazine of The United Reformed Church*

Reynolds (1961)   Reynolds, J. S., *Providence Chapel, Chichester* (The Chichester Papers No. 19, 1961)

Rix (1837)   Rix, S. W., *Brief Records of the Independent Church at Beccles, Suffolk* (1837)

Scott (1888)   Scott, John, *Berwick-upon-Tweed: the History of the Town and Guild* (1888)

Som A&N H Soc   *Proceedings, Somerset Antiquarian & Natural History Society*

Summers (1900)   Summers, W. H., *A Centenary Memorial of the Congregational Church, Beaconsfield* (1900)

UHST   *Transactions of the Unitarian Historical Society* (from 1917)

URCHSJ   *Journal of the United Reformed Church History Society* (from 1973)

Whitehead (1932)   Whitehead, T., *Illustrated Guide to Nidderdale and a History of its Congregational Churches* (1932)

WHSP   *Proceedings of the Wesley Historical Society* (from 1897)

INDEX TO INVENTORY